Young Readers Edition

THE PRIMATES

Sarel Eimerl and Irven DeVore
and the Editors of TIME-LIFE BOOKS

TIME-LIFE BOOKS, NEW YORK

ON THE COVER: Indian grey langurs,
a species of Old World monkeys,
perch in a tamarind tree. Although
well adapted for a life in the trees, the adult
langur often spends most of his day
on the ground.

Contents

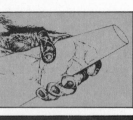

Introduction

In the last few years, great progress has been made in understanding man's closest relatives, the monkeys and the apes. New fossils have been found. Biochemical studies have clarified the relationships of many primates to each other and to man. But perhaps the greatest addition to our information has come in studies of behavior.

An understanding of the social life of monkeys and apes tells us much about our own evolution. For example, the importance of early experience in shaping the emotional makeup of human adults is revealed by experiments on monkeys; how these crucial events take place in a natural state is shown by field studies. This combination of laboratory experiment and observation in the wild offers the scientist the rich insights described in this book.

Research on primate structure and behavior is proceeding rapidly. The U.S. government has set up Primate Centers to accelerate understanding of the primates and their efficient use in medical research. Many investigators are now in the field studying behavior. A book such as this represents an exciting moment in the history of primatology. It states new facts and insights, and at the same time makes clear that many of these will be further modified and enriched as science increases its understanding of the relatives of man.

S. L. WASHBURN
Professor of Anthropology
University of California
Berkeley, California

1
What Is a Primate?

Primate, which means first, is the name man has chosen for the animal order that contains prosimians, monkeys, apes and man himself. From a tiny, shrewlike creature that lived millions of years ago, the primates in time have grown into a dazzling variety of forms. How the primates evolved and how they live today is the subject of primatology, a young science that has gained popularity only in the past few decades. But within this short time primatology has become one of the most important of all the biological sciences.

For many years zoologists classified man among the primates because of the close similarities in body structure between him and other primates, particularly the apes. Recent research also shows that more than the body structure is similar—the cells and

(*Text continued on page 13*)

A HAPPY TARSIER partially shuts its eyes as it enjoys a meal. Tarsiers, which belong to the group of primates called prosimians, are among the smallest primates—about as large as a rat. They once ranged over most of the Northern Hemisphere, but now live only on a few Southeast Asian islands.

7

The Four Primate Groups

Ruffed Lemur

Tree Shrew

Bush Baby

Dwarf Lemur

Aye-aye

Potto

Tarsier

Indri

THE PROSIMIANS, which most resemble the
primitive ancestors of all primates, form the
largest of the four groups. By studying the
prosimians that exist today, as well as the fossils
of those that are now extinct, primatologists
have begun to learn more about what
the original primate ancestor was like.

NEW WORLD MONKEYS (*below*)—those found
in South and Central America—differ from their
Old World cousins in several ways. One of these
differences is in their social structure. While
the Old World monkeys have societies
with leaders and followers, the New World
monkeys are generally less rigidly organized.

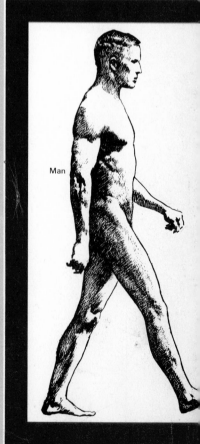

Man

White-headed
Saki

Emperor Tamarin

Woolly Monkey

Black-and-white
Colobus Monkey

Hamadryas Baboon

OLD WORLD MONKEYS, represented at left by two common types, include more varieties and cover a far wider range than New World monkeys. They are plentiful in Africa (but not on nearby Madagascar, where the only primates are prosimians), in Southeast Asia and on many islands in the Malay Archipelago.

APES AND MAN belong to the same group. This does not mean, as some people used to believe, that man is descended from the apes. But most primatologists today do believe that just as all primates derived from a prosimian-like creature, man and the apes also shared a common ancestor who lived about 20 million years ago.

Orangutan

Gibbon

Gorilla

North America

Where the Primates Live

PROSIMIANS

 TREE SHREWS

 LEMUROIDS

 LORISOIDS

 TARSIERS

NEW WORLD MONKEYS

 CEBIDS

MARMOSETS

South America

OLD WORLD MONKEYS

 COLOBUS
AND LANGURS

 BABOONS
AND MACAQUES

 GUENONS
AND MANGABEYS

ANTHROPOID APES

 GIBBONS

 ORANGUTAN

CHIMPANZEES

 GORILLAS

 ▲ NONTROPICAL FOSSILS

10

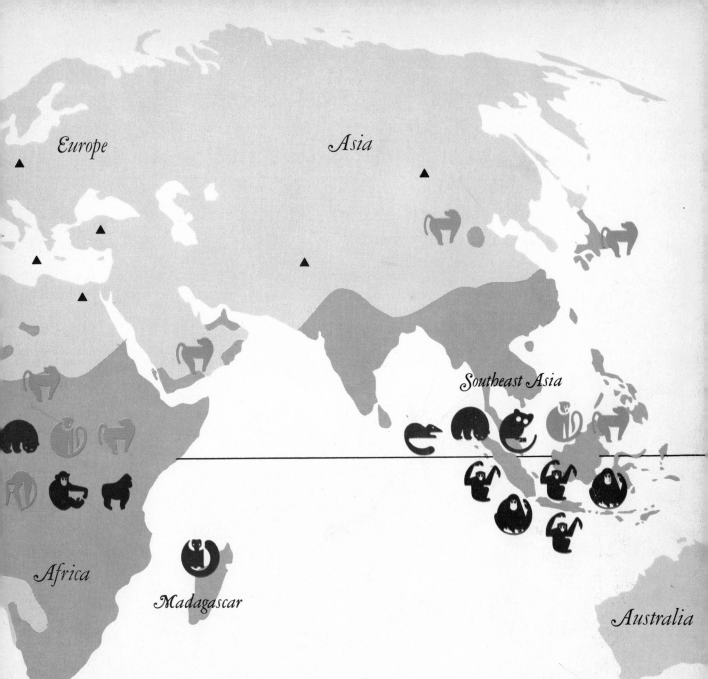

Almost all of the types of primates alive today are
found in the tropical or semitropical lands near the
equator. The regions in which they live are indicated
by dark shading on this map. But the primates
have not always been confined to these areas. Many
fossils of earlier kinds of primates now extinct have
been found in parts of the world that are not all
tropical: the United States, the tip of South America
and the British Isles—places where no primates of
today could easily survive. Some of these fossil

finds resemble one another; for example, teeth found
in Asia match others found in Europe, indicating
that the same kind of chimpanzeelike primate once
ranged throughout both continents. Other fossils
offer clues to what the ancestors of today's primates
looked like. The reason these early primates were
so much more widespread is that the entire earth
was once much warmer. But about 35 million years
ago the climate changed, and the primates living in
those northern and southern lands died out.

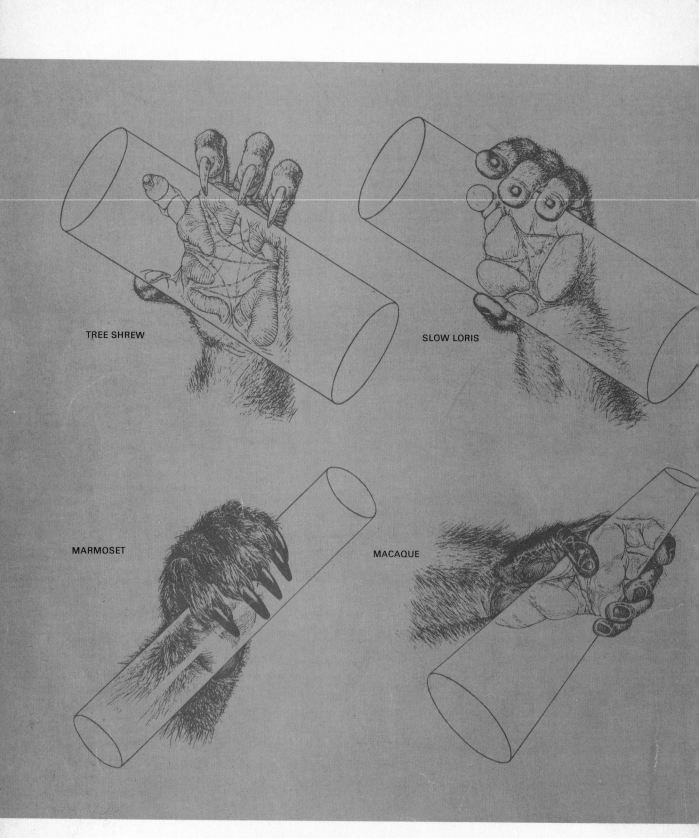

TREE SHREW

SLOW LORIS

MARMOSET

MACAQUE

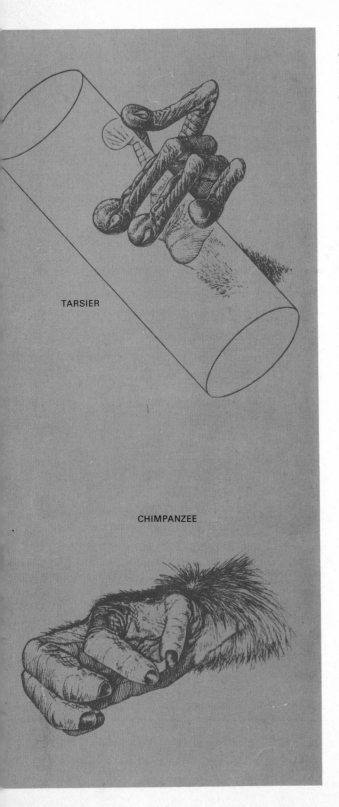

TARSIER

CHIMPANZEE

blood of man and other primates are also closely related. Now, thanks to recent studies of monkeys and apes in their natural environment, it is becoming clear that in their behavior too they are much closer to man than anyone had imagined. Many live in highly organized social groups. Some are ruled by a single, all-powerful leader, others by a select group whose members pass down their power to their offspring. In a group of monkeys some are good friends, others dedicated enemies; some are popular, others disliked. Baby monkeys as they grow up must learn a code of behavior, much as a human child has to do. All the members of a group are linked together by an elaborate system of communication that includes both sounds and gestures. The comparison with human behavior, of course, must not be pushed too far. Yet in their daily routines and in their relationships with their fellows, there are many surprising resemblances between man and the nonhuman primates.

A Show of Hands

All primates have hands with movable fingers, but the shape of the fingers, their position and the way in which they can move differ greatly. Among the prosimians (*top row*), the tree shrew's hand has long claws adapted for digging into branches. The hand of the loris grips like a pincers, and the round pads on the tips of the tarsier's fingers help it to hold onto branches after its long leaps. Among the monkeys and apes (*bottom row*) the marmoset has the clumsiest hand. The macaque and chimpanzee, by contrast, have highly dexterous hands and can pick up objects between their thumbs and fingers, like man.

There are almost 200 living species of primates. They range from creatures as primitive as the insect-eating tree shrew to highly complex man. And since the primate order contains extinct animals as well as the ones that exist today, no single characteristic can be picked out to define the whole group. Tree shrews, for instance, in most respects do not seem to fit in, yet they are included both on the basis of their ancestry and because of certain very special details of the skull. What all primates, living and extinct, do have in common are adaptations for living in the trees.

These adaptations show in the structure of primates' brains and the fact that they have fingers and toes with nails instead of claws; the adaptations also show in the way primates use their senses of smell, sight and touch and in the way they give birth and rear their young. No one species has all these features, but there is one quality that is shared by all except the tree shrews: the ability to climb by grasping.

This talent lies at the root of the whole primate order. Basically, primates are tree-dwelling animals. They came into existence in the trees and developed and prospered there. It was by wrapping their fingers and toes around a branch instead of simply driving their claws into it, as almost all other tree-dwelling mammals do, that the primates were able to make themselves the undisputed masters of the trees.

This ability evolved slowly from modest beginnings, starting with little insect-eaters that probably resembled the present-day tree shrews of Asia. Sixty million years ago these small creatures were already living in the trees. From then on, the story of primate evolution is largely the story of how each successive species improved its ability to move about in the forest canopy. Grasp was the key because grasp meant security. It enabled primates to climb more safely along delicate branches and so expand their range of feeding. It reduced the risk of falling, and because of the superior hold it provided, grasp permitted the primates to grow much larger than they could have if their stability in the trees depended entirely on the strength of their claws.

The process of changing clawed hands into grasping ones started when the primitive insect-eaters developed long, slender fingers and independently moving thumbs. Even in modern tree shrews one can see the beginnings of the primate grasp. A transitional group called prosimians began to evolve. For millions of years, prosimians dominated the forests. They spread across North America, reached Asia and spread into Europe. Later they reached Africa and finally Madagascar. The fossil remains of more than 60 now-extinct kinds of prosimians have already been discovered, and there certainly must have been many others.

The few prosimians that still survive in Africa and Asia do so only because most are nighttime animals and do not compete with the daytime monkeys. One group of

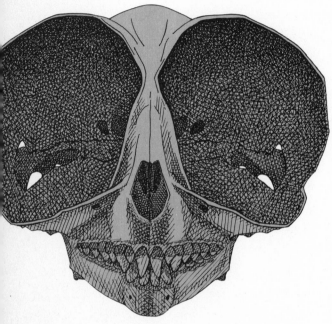

A Pop-eyed Prosimian's Skull

Among the primates the largest eyes, in proportion
to body size, belong to the tarsier. The eye sockets
in this drawing of a tarsier's skull illustrate just
how big they are. If man's eyes were proportionately
as large, they would be the size of small grapefruits.
Because it moves about at night, the tarsier needs
good eyesight to leap from tree to tree.

prosimians, however, made its way from Africa to the nearby island of Madagascar
and to a few smaller islands in the Indian
Ocean. There they found themselves free
of competition from monkeys and any large
meat-eating animals, and they evolved into
several distinct families. Today there are
19 species. Some closely resemble the prosimians of 50 or more million years ago. By
studying both the fossils and the living
forms, primatologists have been able to obtain a fairly accurate impression of man's
remote tree-dwelling ancestors.

All the Madagascar prosimians come under the general heading of lemuroids, which
embrace a wide variety of forms. Some
move around by day, others in the evening,
others only at night. There are primitive
types, the size of mice, which live mainly
on insects. There are more advanced species,
the size of large dogs, which eat leaves,
buds and fruit. Some are solitary, others
highly social. And while lemuroids are four-
footed, one family, the Indriidae, moves
by holding its body upright, even when it
jumps from one tree to another.

It was in their ability to grasp that prosimians moved away from their ancestors. They
acquired thumbs and big toes that were capable of free movement, acting like the
second jaw of a clamp against the other fingers or toes. Their hands and feet were
equipped with flat nails, instead of claws.
While they all secure their hold by grasping,
their ways of moving vary considerably. Except for the upright Indriidae, the lemuroids

use their fingers and toes to give them a
firm hold while they move on all fours
along the tops of branches, rather like monkeys. By contrast, the African galago, or
bush baby, moves in long hops when it is
on the ground, using its hind feet like a kan-
garoo. These creatures are amazingly fast,
agile and accurate. A captive bush baby
has been observed to jump 20 feet downward to land securely on the top of

a door that was only two inches wide.

Other prosimians, the lorises of Asia and
the pottos of Africa, are as slow as the
bush babies are fast; the native word for
the potto is the "softly-softly." They pro-
ceed with great care along the branches,
moving in slow motion as they advance al-
ternate hands and feet. In feeding, lorises
will often hang by their feet with a grip so
strong that they can pull themselves back

The Most Primitive Primates

At the very bottom of the primate ladder are the tree shrews, prosimians found in Southeast Asia. They are fierce little beasts—the caged pair of lesser tree shrews shown above are fighting to decide just whose cage it is. The pentailed tree shrew (*upper right*) is nocturnal, and so has larger eyes and ears than its cousins. The common tree shrew at right, found in Malaysia, looks so much like squirrels there that the natives call both by the one name: *tupai*.

up on a branch without using their arms.

Watching a prosimian is like being transported back to the world of 50 million years ago. In these furry, bushy-tailed little animals we can see the early forms of adaptation to life in the trees. Consider their eyes and their snouts. To a considerable degree, sight and smell work together. Both are used for gathering information, and the more use an animal makes of one, the less it depends on the other. To an animal that lives on the ground and is active at night, smell can be extremely useful; it can identify objects merely by sniffing at them. To an animal that does not live on the ground and is active by day, smell is less important than vision. This is seen particularly well in birds, whose sense of smell is poor but whose vision is keen. Among animals that live in the trees, too, vision is far more valuable than smell, because it helps an animal to avoid falls and to identify food amid the rich and colorful foliage. Just as life in the trees favored better grasp, so it also favored good vision.

The shift from smell to vision characteristic of higher primates can be seen in its halfway stage in a prosimian. Their snouts are less prominent than an insect-eater's. A slightly smaller portion of their brains is devoted to smell and a slightly larger portion to sight. This shift is also reflected in the position of their eyes. Most primitive mammals have eyes set at the sides of their heads so that they can see a

full half circle without turning their heads. But this advantage is offset by a drawback: because their visual fields do not overlap, they cannot judge distance accurately. To such an animal the ability to judge distance may not be important, but to a tree-dwelling primate, it is a matter of life and death. As an adaptation to life in the trees, the eyes of prosimians have moved closer to the fronts of their faces; thus their fields of vision overlap, giving them the ability to see things in depth.

The great advantage of this kind of vision, which is called stereoscopic, is that it enables an animal to see clearly in three dimensions. This kind of acute visual perception permits man to manipulate delicate tools. It helped monkeys to see very clearly the branches they were about to grasp and also, aided by their color vision, to identify any suitable food within reach. Relying as they do on vision, it is natural for monkeys to examine strange objects not by leaning over to sniff at them but by reaching out, grasping them and examining them with their eyes and fingers.

To reach out and seize an object a short distance away may not appear to be difficult. We take it for granted because we are continually performing far harder tasks, such as threading needles or adjusting television sets. But consider the problems it presents to prosimians. They have only what is called "whole-hand control": while they can move their fingers and toes freely, they can only move them together, not in-

How the Tarsier Was Named

In the feet of every primate are bones called
the tarsal bones. In the human foot the
tarsal bones are small, but in the tarsier
they are extremely long (*bottom drawings*),
and it is these bones that gave the animal
its name. The tarsier uses the bones for extra
leverage, giving it an added spring; although
the creature is only the size of a chipmunk,
it can cover six feet in a single leap. Tarsiers
are peculiar in another way—they can swivel
their heads in a full half circle, as the top
one in the photograph at right is doing.

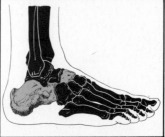

HUMAN FOOT · TARSIER FOOT

19

The Ghosts of Madagascar

On the island of Madagascar, off the east coast of
Africa, live the lemurs, whose name comes from a
Latin word meaning "ghosts." They are noisy
ghosts, scurrying through trees and disappearing,
only to reappear on another branch or in another
tree. Of all lemurs, the four-foot-tall indri (*below*) is
the largest. The tiny mouse lemur, shown at right
sniffing a flower, generally eats insects, but is also
fond of sweets such as fruit and honey.

dividually. When they reach out to grasp a
branch, all five of their digits close over it
together. When they pick up something,
their digits work in the same way.

This way of grasping has limitations, and
the Old World monkeys, as they evolved,
improved upon it. In feeding, grooming and
other specialized activities, natural selection
increasingly favored control of the fingers
and toes. Ultimately monkeys were able to
seize even very small objects between their

thumbs and forefingers. And as monkeys kept improving their ability to grasp, their brains and nervous systems became increasingly elaborate.

Much of the increase in the size of monkeys' brains was devoted to areas controlling their hands and their feet. Most of the rest served to make their vision more acute and their memories larger. Thus monkeys became able to observe the world around them more intelligently. They could see the difference between objects more clearly. They could store up a vast reservoir of visual images. They could summon up, for comparison, a larger number of memories to help them meet any new situations they were faced with. In brief, the monkeys were able to learn more—and therefore they required larger brains.

Because of all these advantages, monkeys displaced the prosimians in many parts of the world, and expanded rapidly throughout

Two Different Kinds of Lemurs

Altogether there are ten types of lemur on Madagascar, and except for those in zoos, they are found nowhere else. Each kind is different. For example, the dwarf lemur (*above*) has a less efficient temperature-regulating mechanism than other primates, including man; its body temperature is rarely above the temperature of the air. The sifaka (*right*) is a close relative of the indri (*previous page*), and like the indri, somewhat resembles a monkey. But although it can bound along the ground and leap great distances through trees, it lacks the monkey's intelligence.

the forests. By about 30 million years ago, one major group had spread across most of South America, while another had developed and spread into southern Asia, southern Europe and Africa. By this time the monkeys had reached their evolutionary peak; their fundamental structure was set, and so was that of their descendants.

The human brain is perhaps a dozen times as large and much more complicated than that of any monkey. But most of this additional brain is devoted to memory, association and speech—that is, to abstractions. In his basic methods of perceiving the world around him, man has advanced hardly at all beyond the stage reached by monkeys some 25 million years ago. He may not react like a monkey, but essentially he

smells, tastes, hears, touches and sees very much as a monkey does.

In body proportions and posture, however, men and monkeys are very different animals. The monkey is four-footed and still has many of the characteristics of primitive four-legged mammals. Its trunk, the part of its body from the neck to the hips, is long, narrow and deep. Some monkeys have limbs attached in such a way that their movements are largely restricted to backward and forward motions such as those used in walking or running. The general proportions of a monkey's trunk are much like those of a dog—and like a dog, a monkey tends to keep its arms and legs parallel. Even when stretching, it will reach out forward, as a dog does when it awakens

from sleep, rises, yawns and stretches out its legs. And in the trees, some monkeys move the way such four-legged animals as squirrels do, walking or running along the top of a branch.

With apes and men movement is quite different. Apelike animals first appeared among the monkeys some 25 to 30 million years ago, somewhere in the forest that at that time existed from Africa across Asia to the East Indies.

Today there are four main groups of apes, divided into two families. One family includes the African gorilla and chimpanzee and their Asiatic relative, the orangutan. The other family is that of the Asiatic gibbons. All are built quite differently from monkeys, and move about in a different way. They have short, wide trunks and long, free-swinging arms that enable them to reach out in all directions in the trees. They grasp and swing their bodies from the branches instead of running on top of them, monkey fashion, on all fours.

It is tempting to think of apes as being two-footed animals that are on the verge of standing erect and moving on their legs alone. But this is an oversimplification. Essentially apes are still as four-legged as monkeys. On the ground they move in many ways, all of them quite different from the way monkeys do. Monkeys walk on the flats of their hands while the chimpanzee and gorilla walk on their knuckles. The orangutan is awkward on the ground and almost never leaves the trees. The gibbon

only occasionally moves on the ground but when it does, it runs about on two legs, its arms held like a tight-rope walker's pole, for balance. Only man, whose pelvis and leg structure are very different from the ape's, walks habitually on two feet.

We are not sure exactly how or why the apes came to move about by swinging from their arms, but they may have developed this talent as a means of obtaining food. Many branches high in the forest are too delicate to bear even the weight of an aver-age-sized monkey moving along them on all fours let alone that of a big ape, but if the weight can be divided by hanging from several branches with two feet and one hand, then a lot of hitherto unreachable food becomes available. And this is the way apes do feed, in perfect comfort.

With the exception of the gibbon, all apes are much bigger than any tree-dwelling monkey. But why did they grow bigger?

There was, of course, a competitive ad-vantage: the advantage that any big animal

Wide-eyed Slowpokes

The laziest-acting members of the prosimian family are the lorises. The two shown here, both natives of Southeast Asia, are the "slow" loris (*left*), and the slender loris. Actually all lorises are slow; and they produce so little heat energy that even in their tropical environment they would die of cold if their thick fur coats were shorn off. The lorises, which move about at night, have big eyes adapted to seeing in the dark as they amble through the trees, eating insects, birds and eggs.

has over a smaller one when it comes to a question of eating or being eaten. Greater size also means an extended life span. Big animals tend to live longer because their rate of metabolism is slower than that of small animals; their internal organs simply do not have to work so hard, and therefore do not wear out so fast.

It is a basic rule of evolution that any useful change leads to more change. The practice of arm-swinging in the apes prompted a series of further changes that altered the primate body. In order to swing more effectively from their arms, the apes acquired different equipment in their shoulders, their elbows and their wrists that made their arm movements much more flexible. Apes can swing their arms out in a wide circle from their shoulders—forward, sideways, backward and up. They can straighten out their arms at the elbow, and their wrists are much more mobile than a monkey's— more so, in fact, than a man's. An ape can hang from a branch by one hand and rotate its body completely around, thanks to the flexibility of its arm and wrist joints.

Nor did the changes that sprouted from their arm-swinging stop at the apes' arms and shoulders. In time the changes affected the whole of the apes' upper bodies, giving them their short spinal column, wide, shallow trunk, and hip bones spread out to provide additional room for the attachment of muscles. All of these changes helped to produce animals that, from the waist up, physically resemble man. From the hips to the skull, an ape looks very much like a man, as one can see by observing an ape from behind while it is eating. Sitting there, reaching for food and carrying it to its mouth, it looks almost exactly like a man helping himself to various dishes at dinner.

Man has always had a tendency to consider his own qualities as being unique. As a result people tend to lump apes together with monkeys as animals that resemble each other, both physically and mentally, much more closely than either resembles man. So far as their intelligence is concerned, this may be accurate enough. But actually man stands physically much closer to an ape than an ape does to a monkey. Although man and apes long ago went their own separate evolutionary ways, man can see in the apes a vision of his own past.

A Champion High Jumper

One of the fastest and most agile of the prosimians is the lesser galago, or "bush baby." It scampers through trees, taking long hops, kangaroo-style, with its powerful hind legs. The bush baby's aim is so good that it has been seen taking a 20-foot jump downward to land on a perch only two inches wide.

2

The Monkeys: Success in the Trees

A SPIDER MONKEY holds tight to a tree trunk high in its leafy home with its hands and feet and tail. Most monkeys are nimble, but the spider monkey is the prize acrobat of all, largely because of its long, powerful tail, which it uses as an arm for anchoring, swinging, and even for picking fruit.

Second only to man, monkeys are the most successful of primates. From the viewpoint of evolution, success is judged by numbers, and monkeys exist not only in vast numbers but also in a dazzling variety of forms. In South America there are monkeys no bigger than kittens—in Africa, monkeys that weigh about as much as Great Danes. Some are as timid as antelopes while others will stand off a hungry cheetah. According to the best estimate, there are 128 species of monkeys. By contrast, living races of men, though they have spread farther than monkeys across the earth, all belong to a single species.

Why is there so much variety among monkeys? It is easiest to begin with the differences that separate one closely related species from another. A species is a group of animals that is reproductively isolated from all other animals—that is, it cannot breed with any others. The members of the group must be the same kind of animals, physically capable of mating with one another and producing offspring. They must also have access to each other. It is the matter of access that helps explain why there

New World Noses

A simple way to tell New World monkeys from those of the Old World is to look at their noses. American monkeys, such as the young howler at right, have round, widely separated nostrils; they are called the Platyrrhini, from the Greek for "broad-nosed."

PLATYRRHINI

is such variety among monkeys. Many of them are tree animals that seldom descend to the ground. Suppose the forest thins out or a stream widens into a river too broad to be crossed in a single leap. The tree monkeys in an isolated area of trees are cut off from other monkeys of their species. As generations pass, changes occur in the monkeys. Those changes that are helpful to survival are passed throughout the isolated group, perhaps bringing a fresh dash of color or a lengthening of the tail. Through time, the processes of change continue to increase the differences between the isolated group and the rest of the species. Eventually reproductive isolation is complete. The isolated group is now sufficiently changed that it can no longer interbreed with the original

group. A new species has emerged.

Variations caused by this process are usually minor at first. But they have over thousands of years created the dazzling variations in design and in coloring—in browns and greens and whites and blues and yellows—that are typical of the tree-dwelling monkeys. The names of some of the guenons, the commonest tree-dwelling monkeys of Africa, suggest this colorful variety: the red-bellied monkey, the moustached monkey, the yellow-nosed monkey, the white-nosed, the spot-nosed, the red-eared, the white-collared, the green, the blue, the owl-faced.

The earliest primates were undoubtedly all very much alike. But once one group of monkeys begins to diverge from another, as

Old World Noses

The monkeys of Africa and Asia, such as the red-eared guenon at left, have a narrow separation between their nostrils. These close-set nostrils are shaped like commas pointing downward, giving the group the name of Catarrhini, Greek for "downward-flowing."

CATARRHINI

the isolated tree-dwellers in our example did, the differences will be multiplied. One basic separation apparently took place at least 40 million years ago, somewhere along the ancestral primate line, to produce two separate families today. One of these is found in Central and South America: the New World monkeys. The other, the Old World monkeys, spread throughout Africa and Asia. Every living monkey belongs to one family or the other. The differences between the two result partly from their long separation and partly from the effects of the environments in which they have lived.

The most urgent problem an individual animal faces is finding food. It must be able to find enough food that it can digest, or it must become adapted so that it can di-

gest the food that is available. The problem is solved in many ways, and this provides a second answer to the question of why there is so much variety among monkeys.

It is on the basis of their digestive systems that all Old World monkeys are divided into two subfamilies: the langurs and colobus monkeys in one group and all other Old World monkeys in the other group. The colobus monkey and the langur are primarily leaf-eaters. Leaves are plentiful but not particularly nourishing. To get the most nourishment from leaves, langurs and colobus monkeys have developed greatly enlarged stomachs. Each has to eat such huge quantities of leaves to survive that after a full meal, the monkey's stomach and meal together make up one fourth or more of its

31

total body weight. At such times a langur's stomach sticks out so far it is hard to tell whether a female is about to give birth or is just well fed.

The advantage of the colobus-langur digestive system is that it enables these monkeys to live on coarse, mature leaves that would give any other monkeys a bad case of indigestion. These old leaves even provide liquid. The Indian langur can go for several months without drinking water. Langurs in general can survive in dry areas where almost any other monkey would perish.

There is a third reason for all these variations. Consider the differences in physical structure and in temperament that distinguish the colobus monkey and the langur from the baboon. The colobus monkey and the langur are extremely timid, and when in danger they usually either hide or flee. They have a typical monkey face; they are long-bodied and slender, and their long arms and legs help make them exceedingly agile. This agility is an adaptation to life in the treetops. A langur can run with ease along slender branches, race from the top to the bottom of a 100-foot tree in a few seconds, and clear a gap of 25 to 30 feet separating one tree from another in a single, surefooted leap.

Baboons are very different. They are large, sturdy and powerful; full-grown males may weigh up to 100 pounds. They are neither slender nor graceful. They are built to maneuver and fight on the ground. Their faces are long, with doglike muzzles and

The Pinocchio of Monkeydom

These Borneo langurs are aptly named proboscis monkeys, from the Latin word for an elephant's trunk. Only adult males develop the long noses, which, surprisingly, do not get in their way when they eat or lap up water (*above*). They often escape the heat by bathing in streams. Sometimes currents and tides carry them out to sea, like the one at right, which was picked up far from shore.

heavy ridges of bone over the eyes. Their bodies are thick, their shoulders heavily muscled and in some species made to appear even more formidable by a thick ruff of hair. Baboons are clumsy in the trees, and cannot leap long distances from one tree to another. They are tough, aggressive, prepared to stay and fight against anything but large animals like lions, and armed men.

Why the differences? The answer in one word is "predators." A predator is an animal that hunts another animal, as a lion hunts an antelope. Food is the first requirement for survival; defense against attack is the second. To tree-dwelling monkeys, defense is not much of a problem. Their chief enemies are meat-eating animals, including snakes and birds of prey—especially the monkey-eating eagle—and, very recently, man. In the trees, monkeys can usually get away from an animal or a snake by sheer agility and speed. By staying below the top branches, they can avoid most attacks by birds. A sturdy body and heavy muscles would be more of a handicap than an advantage, since these would reduce the agility that is so valuable in the trees. Thus, almost all tree-dwelling monkeys are like the colobus monkey and the langur—slender, long-limbed and timid.

Baboons, however, are basically ground-dwelling animals. True, they sleep in trees, often feed in them, and when threatened by predators, climb up into them for refuge. But most of their waking hours are spent on the ground, where they are in constant danger from enemies: lions and jackals, cheetahs and hyenas. As an adaptation to life on the ground, male baboons acquired long teeth with which to defend themselves, their females and their young. They also acquired long, strong jaws to house the teeth. But animals that fight with their teeth also need sturdy trunks and powerful shoulder muscles. Male baboons have all these; what is more, they frequently fight together against a common enemy.

Still, hefty and muscular as they are, baboons cannot always be sure of winning a fight against, say, a leopard. Even if they do win, they are liable to get badly mauled in the process. Obviously they are better off if they can prevent predators from starting an attack. One way they do this is by bluffing, by giving the impression that they are more ferocious than they really are. The ruff of hair around a male baboon's shoulders achieves exactly this purpose. It makes the baboon's whole body look wider and deeper, and thus encourages predators to think twice before launching an attack.

Adaptation to environment also explains the pads of toughened skin that Old World monkeys have on their rumps, just beneath the tail. These pads are related to sleeping posture. An animal is most vulnerable while sleeping, and even the trees are not a completely safe refuge against attack. Certain snakes and hunting animals, notably the night-prowling leopard, are good climbers and they can move swiftly and silently.

Pads for Resting

Callous rump pads are among the characteristics of Old World monkeys. These tough, flat areas on the undersides of the haunches make it easy for a monkey to wedge itself in the fork of a tree (*above*) to sleep—or to balance on a slender limb while it eats, as the Kirk's red colobus monkey of Zanzibar is doing at left.

Timid Leaf-Eaters

Africa's black-and-white colobus monkey
(*left*) and its rare Asian cousin the golden
langur (*above*) both live deep in the forest
and eat plants. The black-and-white
colobus was nearly hunted to extinction
for its fur. The golden langur is so shy
that although the species had been heard
of in 1907, it took 46 years to find and
photograph one. Its golden winter coat
changes to a creamy white each summer.

Monkeys, therefore, tend to sleep as far away from the tree trunks as they can, out on the slenderest branches that will bear their weight. Then if a snake or a cat ventures out toward them, they will be warned by the swaying of the branch. But sleeping on a narrow branch presents its own problem. If a monkey just stretches out like a man in bed, it is likely to fall. To assure their balance, monkeys sleep sitting on their rumps with their legs thrust upward at a sharp angle, clinging to another branch for additional support. Because the pads of skin are attached directly to the bones, replacing soft, sensitive tissue between bone and skin, monkeys can sit comfortably on them for hours.

Apart from baboons and possibly gorillas, there are only a few nonhuman primates that, when threatened, stay and fight instead of fleeing or hiding. One of these, the macaque, lives in Asia, and although smaller is much like the African baboon. It, too, lives mainly on the ground and has acquired the same kind of body build and temperament for precisely the same reason: to defend itself against predators.

Scientists have found that Old World monkeys and New World monkeys differ in the structure of their blood, in the number and shape of their teeth, the form of their brains and their ability to grasp and swing by their tails. Since they have physical differences, it seemed logical that they might also have different patterns of behavior.

Studies of several species of South American monkeys, both in the field and in captivity, showed them to be mild and unaggressive, so New World monkeys in general were judged to be friendly and peaceful creatures. Old World monkeys got quite another reputation. In the late 1920s, a hundred hamadryas baboons from Africa were placed together in the London Zoo. Hamadryas baboons are fierce-looking creatures with large manes. They form groups composed of one male and several females and their young; the male "herds" the females, punishing them if they stray, and fights off intruding males.

Given these characteristics, the situation in the London Zoo was an impossible one. Not only was the place overcrowded to begin with, but worse still, there were many more males than there were females. With no chance to form their regular groups, the males, who were naturally aggressive, were bound to fight. And fight they did, with such ferocity that within a few years more than half of them were killed.

The way the male hamadryas baboons behaved inside their enclosure suggested two conclusions. One was that baboon society was built on sex and jealousy. The other was that the males were always fighting over who should dominate. Stronger males seized food from weaker ones, threatened them, attacked them, drove them into corners, and in general kept them in a state of terror.

(*Text continued on page 40*)

MANED MARMOSETS

TAMARINS

CALLIMICOS

DOUROUCOULIS

TITIS

SQUIRREL MONKEYS

TRUE MARMOSETS

PYGMY MARMOSETS

Marmosets

Cebid Monkeys

Platyrrhines

A Family Tree
of New World Monkeys

SAKIS

UAKARIS

HOWLERS

WOOLLY MONKEYS

CAPUCHINS

SPIDER MONKEYS

The American monkeys, or playtyrrhines, are divided into two groups, as indicated by the big fork in the trunk of this family tree. At left are the marmosets, the smallest New World monkeys, the tiniest of which is the pygmy marmoset, three to four inches long without its tail. Marmosets scamper through the branches like squirrels, while the cebids, at right, leap or swing from tree to tree. The large and varied cebid family is divided into two categories: those with prehensile, or grasping, tails and those without. Four of the five prehensile-tailed types are shown with tails curled above.

39

The next detailed study to be made of Old World monkeys led to false conclusions. It was carried out with a group of macaques transported from their home in India to the 37-acre island of Santiago, just off the coast of Puerto Rico. The macaques did not seem to fight as savagely as the captive hamadryas in London. For one thing, the monkeys had more space, permitting weaker animals to escape from the stronger ones instead of being cornered by them. Nonetheless, the males were obviously competing with each other and used their teeth vigorously in battles for dominance. The most

powerful ones monopolized the females, hogged the food, and just as the stronger hamadryas had done, imposed their will on the weaker males.

Both these studies seemed at the time to suggest that, compared to the monkeys of South America, the Old World monkeys were domineering, aggressive and vicious fighters. From these studies of monkeys in artificial situations it was quite wrongly concluded that *all* Old World monkeys lived in sex-dominated, autocratic societies in which the adult males' only concern was to

Chirpers and Roarers

The maned marmoset (*left*), which is about as big as a squirrel, grasps branches with its clawlike nails. When marmosets twitter and chirp, hidden in the trees, they can be mistaken for birds. The black howler monkey (*right*) is one of the noisiest animals for its size in the world. Its growling roar bursts into drumlike booms that can be heard a mile away.

compete for the females, and that the status of other members of the troops was little better than that of slaves.

Thus the whole world of monkeys was split neatly in two by scientists: the more advanced monkeys of the Old World were all unpleasant, and existed in a state of permanent war, while the more primitive but easy-going South American monkeys lived together in harmony and mutual goodwill.

The only spark of truth in this analysis is that some monkeys are more aggressive than others. But the differences are not between Old World and New World monkeys.

African and Asian tree-dwellers are just about as easy-going as South American ones. The differences are between monkeys that live on the ground and monkeys that live in trees. The true distinction lies between the baboons and macaques and all the rest of the monkeys. These two species have acquired an adaptation of great importance: a temperament that enables them to fight for their way of life instead of fleeing.

How important this temperament is—fully as important as long canine teeth and big muscles—can be seen from the numbers of baboons and macaques that populate the regions where they live. Numbers, let us not forget, are the mark of success in evolution, and in this respect the baboons and macaques are certainly the most successful ground-dwelling monkeys.

There are, of course, other successful adaptations to ground living: the gorilla, which makes up for its lack of aggressiveness by sheer size and strength, and the patas monkey, which instead of fighting runs away or hides. But the baboons and macaques show how selection can work to favor not only a useful physical characteristic but a psychological one as well. And while this adaptation of temperament affected their behavior toward each other as well as toward intruders of other species, it must be realized that they seldom behave in the wild with the ferocity described earlier in the abnormal situations.

The exaggerated view of baboon and macaque ferocity inspired by these two studies actually arose from the failure to realize just how much a monkey's behavior changes when it is kept in captivity. A captive monkey is simply not a normal monkey. It does not even have to be kept in a cage for its behavior to become abnormal. Whenever monkeys are subjected to unnatural conditions—when they are fed, for example, by humans—they are liable to become unusually competitive and aggressive. It is not hard to see why. In the wild, every monkey forages for itself, and competition over food is rare. But if a whole troop of monkeys is obliged to feed out of the same bin, their competitiveness comes out. The closer their confinement, the more aggressive the monkeys will be. They are very much like humans, who become more irritable in a crowded place like Manhattan than in the wide-open spaces of Wyoming. Even the peaceful monkeys, such as Indian langurs, are more nervous and irritable in confined areas around villages than they are in the roomy spaces of the forest.

The captive baboons and macaques were aggressive for yet another reason. In the wild, a monkey learns its place in the group as it grows up. By the time it is adult, it has established a relationship with all the other monkeys. They are all old friends, or at least old acquaintances. Every monkey knows that it is stronger than some, weaker than others. As a result, it is less likely to get into fights in which the outcome is predictable failure.

On the rare occasions that a baboon or a macaque does join another group, it often gets involved in battles that continue until its status is established, much as young boys do when they first attend a new school. It was therefore inevitable that hamadryas baboons suddenly thrown together should have behaved viciously. Just like humans, when aggressive animals find themselves in a strange situation without a familiar order, they struggle for power.

The adaptation of the baboons and macaques that makes it possible for them to

A Fifth Limb

The most useful of all primate tails
belongs to the American spider
monkey. Truly an extra limb, this
supple tail is strong enough to hang
by *(left)* and so sensitive that it
can probe for, find and pick up an
object as small as a peanut *(close-
up, left)*. The tip's hairless underside
has ridges that strengthen its grasp.
Tails are so important to spider
monkeys that they even "hold tails"
instead of holding hands; babies
often clasp tails with their mothers.

stand and fight has enabled them to spread over much of the Old World. They have ranged over a far larger area, in fact, than any other kind of monkey or ape. This shows dramatically how aggressiveness can help an animal extend its habitat. And it brings us back to the curious point that of all the 190 species of primates none has been able to spread over as great an area as the single species of man.

Man has been able to range widely for four main reasons. He is a ground-dwelling animal, not restricted to the forest. He can cross any natural barriers, such as deserts, oceans, rivers and mountains. He can live off a wide variety of foods. Most important of all, he has developed culture. He has learned to make clothes and build fires, and these allow him to live in climates in which he would otherwise perish.

To a considerable degree, man shares the first three of these advantages with the ground-living baboons and macaques. They too can move over unforested land. They too can cross natural barriers such as rivers, because they can swim. They too can digest many kinds of food. With these advantages, baboons have spread across Africa from Dakar in the west to Ethiopia in the east, and south all the way to the Cape of Good Hope. Macaques have done as well or better. One species, the rhesus macaque, is equally at home in forests, in open farmlands and inside heavily populated cities. Another species, the crab-eating macaque, lives in the mangrove swamps of Indonesia. Macaques range high in the Himalayas, and in Japan they dig for plants under the winter snow and in summertime pick up shellfish on the beaches. Were it not for the cold in some areas, for the oceans and the presence of competitors, including man, they might well have spread over as much of the earth as man himself has done.

A Troop of Squirrel Monkeys

Out on a limb, a group of squirrel monkeys scrambles
in a favorite spot: a tall tree, decked with vines
bearing a variety of edible flowers and fruit.
Although they cannot hang by their long, heavy
tails, the squirrel monkeys use them to help keep
balance while they jump from tree to tree.

3

The Apes: Pioneers on Two Legs

In 1840 an English naturalist named William Charles Martin wrote about a female gibbon he had been studying, "to convey in words an idea of the quickness and graceful address of her movements: they may indeed be termed aerial as she seems merely to touch in her progress the branches among which she exhibits her evolutions." No one since has suggested more vividly the sense of flowing rhythm that makes a gibbon in the trees one of the most graceful sights nature has to offer.

The gibbon is an ape—a member of the family that also contains the orangutan, the chimpanzee and the gorilla. The picture of the gibbon as a graceful acrobat flying through the treetops forms a sharp contrast to the popular idea of apes as large, clumsy, blundering creatures. But then apes, like monkeys, are difficult to generalize about.

A GROUP OF GORILLAS relaxes in the lower branches of a jungle tree after a morning devoted to eating. Some groups contain as many as 30 gorillas, but smaller groups of about a dozen members are more common. Despite their size and apparent fierceness, gorillas are normally gentle.

47

Gibbons hurtle around just below the top canopy of densely clustered trees that reach more than a hundred feet high. As a result they are very difficult to study. We know they live in small groups consisting of a male and female and their young. We know that both males and females are so jealous of members of the same sex that the young are forced by one or the other of their parents to go off on their own as soon as they are mature. We know that each separate group keeps intruders at a distance by issuing loud, warning hoots.

Even less is known about orangutans. Although like the gibbons they live in trees, they are slow and deliberate in their movements. Orangs have some very curious characteristics, both in their physical makeup and in the way they move. In the trees, they climb around with ease, using their hands and feet almost interchangeably and with great flexibility. On the ground, they walk very awkwardly; although they go on all fours, their arms are much longer than their legs. As a result their bodies are raised up as they move, giving them the look of an old man, bent by age and making his way with the aid of two sticks.

Orangs once ranged over a much wider area than they now occupy. Today there

are only a few thousand still outside captivity, scattered across some 2,000 square miles of the dense Borneo forests and in the northern tip of Sumatra. They are continually hunted, usually for zoos. Unless some way can be found to stop the hunting, all the orangs not in captivity may soon disappear, and we may no longer be able to study them in their wild home.

Until very recently, the gorilla was practically as unknown as the orang. What is worse, it was thoroughly misunderstood. The misunderstanding was natural enough. Nature has typecast the gorilla for the villain's role. It looks ferocious. A full-grown

King of the Swingers

The ability to "brachiate," or swing hand over hand through the trees, is common to all apes, but none has mastered it as well as the gibbon. The technique is illustrated here in a multiple photograph of a gibbon in captivity moving along a rope. Releasing one hand, it swings swiftly forward and grasps the rope ahead of its other hand, then repeats the process in a continuous forward motion.

adult male stands about six feet tall and weighs more than 400 pounds. Much of this weight is in its mighty chest and massive arms, which suggest that it could hug a man to death. Its face is, if anything, even more menacing. It has huge teeth and a massive jaw, supported by a heavy ridge of bone around the skull. More than that, it beats its chest and pretends to charge when alarmed—a terrifying sight to anyone suddenly confronted by it.

In the eastern Congo and western Uganda, thick tropical forest encircles the slopes of two mountain ranges. This forest is the home of the mountain gorilla. Today some 5,000 to 15,000 gorillas live there in danger of extinction, forced to retreat steadily farther up the mountain sides as the lower slopes are occupied by man and turned over to his cattle.

Early in 1959 two zoologists from the University of Wisconsin, John Emlen and George Schaller, went to West Africa to find out what gorillas were really like. Emlen left after completing his study. Then, Schaller, accompanied by his wife, established himself on the mountain slopes of the Albert National Park and stayed on until September 1960. Each day Schaller ventured out to follow and observe the gorillas. He has described what he found in two magnificent books, *The Mountain Gorilla* and *The Year of the Gorilla*. They contain practically everything that is known about gorillas in the wild. All the statements in this book about gorillas in their natural

Limber Forelimbs

One basic difference between apes and monkeys is that apes can swing their forelimbs much more freely. Most monkeys are really quadrupeds, or four-footed animals. Like the macaque at right, they travel on all four limbs and need only move their front limbs backward and forward (*colored lines*), with just a bit of sideways motion. Apes, like the gibbon on the opposite page, can swing by their arms and move them around freely.

surroundings have been drawn from them.

Schaller discovered that, far from being ferocious beasts, gorillas are actually mild-mannered vegetarians and like to mind their own business. At first they were startled by Schaller's intrusion. Usually when he appeared, an adult male would rise and give a roar of alarm or beat his chest threateningly at Schaller before fading into the trees after the females and the young. But once they realized he was not dangerous, curiosity replaced fear. While Schaller observed them, they observed him.

Occasionally Schaller blundered into a gorilla coming out of the trees. He had already noticed that some gorillas would shake their heads almost in embarrassment when he stared at them. So he decided to try the same thing in tense moments. Whenever he accidentally came face to face with a male gorilla, Schaller would shake his head vigorously—and the gorilla would turn and move off back into the forest. Actually gorillas have little reason to be ferocious. While their ancestors were probably in danger from predators when they first descended from the trees, today's males are so large and powerful that a group is never at-tacked, except very rarely by a leopard.

Its sheer size makes climbing trees an awkward business for an adult gorilla, especially a male. While young gorillas nip around with ease in the trees, adults climb with caution. Even so, branches do break under their weight and they may fall several feet before gaining a secure hold. Actually the adults spend about four fifths of their time on the ground and climb trees only for a specific purpose: to eat, to obtain a longer view or to sleep. Like orangs and chimpanzees, they build nests to sleep in. But while chimpanzees may sleep 100 feet up in the trees, gorilla nests, if built in trees, are rarely more than 10 feet up.

With nothing to fear—except man—and plenty of food available, the gorillas Schaller encountered lived a fairly calm and peaceful life. Most of them lived in groups of from six to 17, each one led by a powerful silver-back male, so called for the silver hairs that sprout up among the black ones when a male gorilla reaches the age of 12 or so. His power over the group is absolute, but normally friendly. Occasionally a young gorilla will get too frolicsome and an adult

The Vanishing Orangutan

Munching on pandanus fruit, a five-year-old orangutan sits happily in the jungle of Sarawak, on the island of Borneo, off the coast of Southeast Asia. Orangutans, highly intelligent apes, have been hunted so long as scientific specimens, and for zoos, that today only a few thousand survive in the wild.

An Ape's Limbs . . .

Apes such as the gibbon have long, strong arms for swinging easily through the trees. The distance from the gibbon's shoulder to its fingertips is almost as great as the distance from its shoulder to its feet.

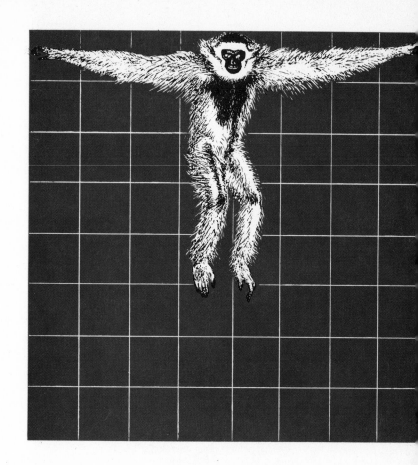

will silence him with a glare or a slap on the ground. Sometimes a couple of females will begin to scream at each other until the leader glares at them and they promptly calm down. When he wants quiet, he gets quiet, but the leaders are usually not very stern. Females nestle against them and babies crawl happily over their huge bodies. When a band of gorillas is at rest, the young play, the mothers tend their infants, and the other adults lie and soak up the sun.

Schaller, as he got to know gorillas better, was more and more impressed by their resemblance to humans. They yawn and stretch when they awake in the morning, and sit, dangling their legs over the sides of their nests. They pick their noses, and scratch themselves when puzzled. If they are nervous or excited, they often begin to eat vigorously, much as a man might pull at a cigarette. Schaller has no doubt that they experience emotions much the same as humans—annoyance, uneasiness, curiosity, boldness. Though individual gorillas have different temperaments, they all seem to have a curious reserve, as if they did not want to show their feelings. It is almost as if they were shy.

Nonetheless, gorillas can exhibit strong feelings, especially when they feel threat-

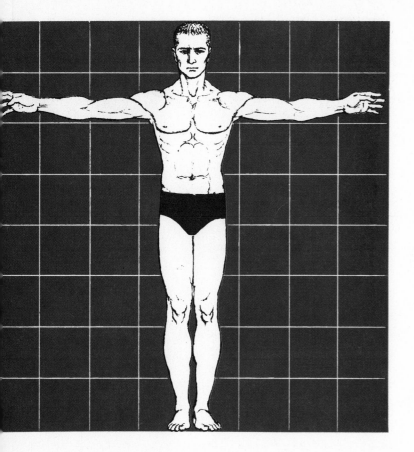

. . . Compared to Man's

Unlike apes, man depends almost
entirely on his legs to get around.
Thus man's legs are long and strong.
While the ape's arms reach nearly to
the ground, man's arms reach only
between his waist and knees.

ened. They scream in alarm, as a warning
to other members of the group. They toss
leaves in the air. They beat their chests.
All gorillas, even very young ones, do this,
rising up on two legs on the ground, or pop-
ping up amid the leaves of a tree to give a
few brief slaps before fading out of sight.

This display seems to serve a variety of
purposes. It may be self-assertion, threat
or challenge—or all three rolled into one. Although this habit has contributed to the
gorilla's reputation for fearsomeness, it is
not so much an act of aggression as a sub-
stitute for it. An angry gorilla may bluff
and threaten another gorilla but he rarely

fights. Schaller describes one incident that
illustrates the point to perfection. Normally,
two strange groups of gorillas will pass each
other and even mix without any signs of
hostility. But once, when two such groups
came together, one leader apparently felt
that his position was threatened and he
tried to cow the leader of the other group.
Several times he rushed at his rival, stop-
ping only an inch away with his head thrust
forward, trying to stare the other silverback
down. His supreme effort was to throw a
handful of leaves in the air in a gesture of
challenge. But when the other male refused
to be frightened, the first silverback gave

up his attempts and retreated. His threatening behavior had avoided a fight.

Chimpanzees, the other kind of African ape, are smaller and less ferocious-looking than gorillas, live the greater part of their lives in trees, and eat fruit rather than leaves. Like tree-dwelling monkeys, chimpanzees are noisy. They seem to love noise for its own sake, and very little is needed to provoke them into a chorus of hoots and high-pitched screams that soon transforms the forest into bedlam.

Most of our information about chimpanzees in the wild comes from a husband-wife team, Vernon and Frances Reynolds, who studied chimpanzees in Uganda, and from Jane and Hugo van Lawick, who observed them in northern Tanzania. Jane van Lawick's principal weapons were an intense determination and a deep affection for chimpanzees. There were between 100 and 200 of these animals in the Gombe Stream Chimpanzee Reserve, where they launched their study—all of them wild, afraid of humans and as anxious to keep away from her as she was to get close to them. It took her about 14 months of patient daily tracking before she could approach to within 30 or 40 feet of them without disturbing their normal activities. Finally she broke down their fear of her entirely and became accepted as one of the group. She was able, for instance, to pick burrs from the hair of certain of the animals, a service which they also performed for her.

The van Lawicks have filmed one of the most puzzling chimpanzee displays, a per-

formance they have called the "rain dance." Jane van Lawick tells of watching a group of chimpanzees in a tree halfway up the side of a steep valley; when rain started falling, the chimpanzees came down from the tree and started walking up the grassy slope. When they reached the top, the females and juveniles climbed high into the trees. Then, as the rain turned into a violent storm, the males, amid crashes of thunder, began their spectacular display. One, turning suddenly, charged down the slope, slapping the ground as it went. As though this were a signal, all the other males joined in. Some charged down, hitting at vegetation. Others sprang into the trees, tore off great branches, hurled themselves to the ground and raced down the hillside at breakneck speed, dragging the branches behind them.

A Tightrope Artist

Using its excellent natural sense of balance, a gibbon finds that the shortest distance from here to there is along a vine—and calmly walks up it. No other ape could perform such a feat, and even the nimblest of the monkeys would use all fours. Among the apes only gibbons have remained small and light. Thus they are in little danger from attackers, which they can easily outdistance, and they can gather food among the smaller branches at the treetops where no other primate would dare to venture.

The Gentle Giants

Gorillas are basically peace-loving creatures, fighting only when they are threatened. The baby above, though old enough to sit by itself and sample tender plant shoots, is within easy reach of its elders—like the big male pictured at right—which will protect it if a predator attacks. In the photograph on the opposite page a protective mother holds on tight to an infant and glares at the camera.

At the bottom, each chimpanzee swung up into a tree to break its headlong flight, then climbed down and began plodding up the hill to repeat its downward rush. Then, as suddenly as it began, the show was over; the spectators climbed down from the trees and the whole group disappeared over the horizon.

What provokes chimpanzees to put on such a performance? Possibly it is an expression of anger at the rain. Possibly it is also a form of sexual display. But there may be more involved than mere anger or showing off. Activities like dancing—including chimpanzee "dancing"—are expressions of high spirits. And chimpanzees are the "show-offs" among the apes. Like humans, they revel in applause; they love attention.

Any animal that wants an audience must be ready to please it. So as one might expect, chimpanzees, while they are young, are the most obliging of the apes. They do very well in laboratory intelligence tests, both because they are intelligent and because they are willing to help. Chimpanzees have learned to ride bicycles and put on evening dress. As a publicity stunt, they have been trained to work on assembly lines, stuffing foam rubber into pillows and putting beds into cartons. They can drive

STANDING UPRIGHT

SYMBOLIC FEEDING

HOOTING

When a Gorilla Gets Annoyed

Probably the most fearsome aspect of a gorilla, aside from its tremendous bulk, is its famous chest-beating act. Actually, beating its chest is only one of a series of actions a male gorilla may use to express anger, fear or annoyance. At first it may simply hoot at an intruder to scare it off (*above*). Next it may turn aside to nibble at food, an action in which the gorilla shows its own uncertainties. Then it may stand up, hurl branches, thump its chest and then the ground—the final and most frightening of the threats. Often when one male begins such a display, others in the group will join in, and even the infants may play a part.

HURLING BRANCHES

CHEST BEATING

LEG KICKING

tractors and they can steer automobiles. In fact, in December of 1963, a Florida police patrol picked up a chimpanzee for speeding.

Actually, the chimp was only steering. Its owner, a carnival showman, was operating the pedals. Still, it would be hard to imagine a gorilla steering a car or driving a tractor, or performing on television. This is not because a gorilla lacks the intelligence to perform such feats; it is just that it lacks the temperament. Its brain, so far as we can tell, is as well developed as a chimpanzee's. Professor Robert M. Yerkes, one of the founding fathers of primatology who carried out many classic studies of captive apes, came to the conclusion that his test gorilla, a young female, was slow at intelligence tests because she was timid and lacked the chimpanzees' interest in winning her keepers' good opinions. Being reserved and self-sufficient, gorillas just may not be prepared to perform the kind of tests that humans devise to satisfy human curiosity.

There is another reason that laboratory tests can be misleading. All too often in the past, they tested abilities that seemed important to humans but did not happen to be at all important to monkeys or apes.

Suppose a New Yorker were trapped by a group of chimpanzees, shipped to Africa and stuck up in a tree a hundred feet above the ground. Practically all his abilities—his mastery of language, his skill at fixing a broken fuel pump, his salesmanship—would be useless in the situation. Hanging on for dear life, often confusing edible with poisonous plants, and no doubt experiencing grave difficulties in distinguishing one chimpanzee from another, he would appear to his captors an exceedingly stupid animal. Their judgment, of course, would be unfair. They would fail to appreciate that New Yorkers are not used to living in trees.

RUNNING SIDEWAYS

UPROOTING BUSHES

GROUND THUMPING

The fact of the matter is that intelligence is not a single thing. What is really important is an animal's ability to learn. Animals have developed the ability to learn things that are important to them and important to survival of the species. Furthermore, in the course of evolution certain abilities have decreased while others have increased in efficiency. A blindfolded man, relying on his sense of smell alone, would fail at making many distinctions that would be easy for a lemur. If the lemur were testing human intelligence, it might mark out a scent trail through the branches of a tree, only to discover that the man was too "stupid" to follow the trail at all. In the same way, chimpanzees are different from men in their ability to use tools and language. Their ability to use tools is very limited, and though great efforts have been made to teach them, they can learn the meaning of only a very few words, and cannot talk at all.

What field studies do show is that apes and monkeys have learned to live rich and complicated lives. They learn to distinguish many different kinds of food plants. They learn the problems of hunters, the social order and the way of life of the group. And just as the behavior of one group of humans varies from another, so the behavior of one troop of monkeys or apes will be different from another troop.

We often think of apes and monkeys as creatures without the power of thinking in concepts. This may be true, though it may be just a question of degree. We know they have the ability to plan—so can we say they do not think about the past and the future? Certainly they learn from the past. We may think of them as worried only about their immediate needs: obtaining food, avoiding danger, getting along with their fellows, raising their young. But is this not largely true of humans too? Professor Adriaan Kortlandt once watched a chimpanzee gazing at a sunset for a full 15 minutes, sitting quietly and watching the changing colors until the western sky grew dark. Was the professor being romantic? Perhaps. Yet surely it would be very arrogant of man to assume that he, and only he, can feel a sensation of awe or pleasure in the beauty of an African twilight.

The Old Man of the Forest

Like a wise village elder, a bearded male orangutan stares thoughtfully into the camera lens—almost as though it were about to give the photographer a bit of intelligent advice. It is this pensive expression that has led the natives of the island of Borneo to call the orangutan "the man of the forest."

CLUTCHING HER INFANT, a gibbon demonstrates
the intense maternal care that all primates give
their young until they are weaned. At birth a gibbon
is almost as helpless as a human baby, but in a few
weeks it grabs, smells and tastes anything it can
reach. In a year the youngster is on its own.

64

4

Trials and Rewards of Childhood

Any event that happens regularly is accepted by us as a matter of course. That is why we never question the normal human practice of bearing one infant at a time. With us it is twins that are the surprise. Triplets are an astonishment, quadruplets command headlines, and quints make their parents fortunes. Yet multiple births are common among mammals, with the multiplication sometimes running as high as two dozen or more babies at a time. Why then does a human female bear twins in only one out of 90 pregnancies, triplets in one out of 8,000, quads in one out of 700,-000, quints in one out of over 65 million? Why do human females experience multiple births about as rarely as monkeys and apes?

The form of the last question helps give the answer. There is much of the monkey in us still. Unlike many prosimians and marmosets, most monkeys came to bear their young singly as a part of their adaptation to life in the trees. It is not possible to say precisely why, but it was partly a solution to the problem of transportation. Throughout the day, monkeys are continually on the move from one feeding area to another.

3 WEEKS

5 MONTHS

The mother of a newborn infant is able to move freely and comfortably, using all four limbs, only because she has a single infant and because that infant does not need to be held; it clings to her hair, either to her front or, as in the case of some South American monkeys, to her back.

To infant monkeys, a strong grasp is almost as vital as breathing. They have to cling to mothers who are likely at any moment to perform some violent feat of acrobatics, either in the normal course of feeding or to escape from sudden danger. A gibbon, for example, even with a newborn infant clinging to her, remains an extraordinarily agile animal. She will feed at the end of a long branch, perhaps swaying in a high

wind. Suddenly she will drop to another branch, run along it, and then start to swing again, taking long leaps that may span 20 feet at a time. The infant cannot afford to relax its grip on her hair for a second because if it does and is shaken loose, it is a dead gibbon.

While the simple act of clinging may not seem very rewarding, it happens to give infant monkeys an enormous amount of pleasure. They prefer an object to which they can cling to one they can suck on. This may seem surprising, but it was proved by Professor Harry Harlow of the University of Wisconsin as a result of experiments with infant rhesus macaques and two simple types of "dummy mothers." These dummies were cylinder-shaped objects made of wire

10 MONTHS

The Baboon Color Shift

A baboon is born with a pink face, pink ears and a black coat of fur. Adult baboons react strongly to these colors: a baby is cared for by its mother, fondled by other females, and protected fiercely by the males. At four months the infant's face begins to darken and its coat turns brown; the females now start to lose interest in it, but the males still protect it. At 10 months the youngster is colored like an adult; it often leaves its mother's side to play.

mesh and equipped with wooden heads and artificial breasts. Half of the dummies were left with their wire bodies bare, while the others were covered with terry cloth. Then he set up a number of cages with pairs of dummy mothers. In half of the cages he connected the "breasts" of the wire dummy to a milk supply; in the other half the terry-cloth mother was the one who had the milk. Finally he put a new-born baby rhesus macaque into each cage and sat back to see what would happen.

There were several things that the babies might have done. They might have ignored the dummy mothers altogether, only going to them to feed. Or they might have developed a special attachment to the dummy whose breast they fed from, and remained near it between their meals. This presumably is what they would do if suckling is the strongest tie binding an infant to its mother. Actually the infants followed a third course. All of them, including those fed from the wire mother, showed an unmistakable preference for the cloth-covered mother and passed hour after hour huddled against it, clinging to the cloth. The cloth, in brief, gave pleasure, security and emotional support; the nipple satisfied only when the infant had to suckle.

The infants displayed a very strong urge not just to grasp, but also to huddle against the cloth. This urge also reflects the situation an infant monkey confronts in the wild. It must obtain food and it must have protection. The source of both is its mother,

67

A Langur Family Circle

Adult male langurs, such as the one eating alone on a branch at left, stay apart from infants. Quite unlike the fatherly baboons, they usually do not go to a baby's rescue even in times of great danger. But grown females, youngsters of both sexes and infants form tight social units. In groups like the one at right, which includes females, a juvenile and a baby, infants meet other langurs their own age and start learning how to live in monkey society.

and therefore the closer it stays to her the safer and better fed it will be. Not only that, it likes to huddle against her because this makes it feel secure.

Does this good feeling come merely because it has learned that the mother's presence means protection? The truth is not so simple. As Harlow showed in another series of experiments, the sense of reassurance an infant monkey obtains from its mother is not derived from her living, breathing, loving presence alone; it is derived in large part from the texture of her body. Taking his infant rhesus macaques out of their cages, Harlow placed them in a large room that contained several strange objects, such as doorknobs and pieces of paper, and one

he knew would scare the infants silly: a toy Teddy bear that when wound up advanced across the floor, beating a drum. The infants were terrified. Some crouched with their hands over their heads while others threw themselves face down on the floor, screaming. Then Harlow added to the scene the cloth-covered mothers the infants had grown used to. Instantly everything was changed. The babies rushed to the mother and buried their heads against the cloth. Then, reassured and curious rather than fearful, they wandered off cheerfully to play with the very objects that had terrified them a few moments before. What is more, in tests in which the terry-cloth mother was put in full view but inside a transparent box, Professor Harlow showed that the in-

fants did not even have to be able to touch her; so long as they could see her they felt confident.

Although monkeys and humans are really two very different types of animal, there are many patterns of behavior that are quite similar, especially in the young. Take for example the common Indian langur. We know a great deal about this monkey from field studies carried out by the anthropologist Phyllis Jay. In October 1958 she went out to India, and during the next two years she concentrated on four separate groups of langurs. At first she spent a great deal of time merely trailing them around, trying to keep them in sight, before they began to get over their fear of her. Eventually the langurs got so used to her pres-

ence that she did not disturb them at all. Most of the adults ignored her, but many females would huddle against her, hoping to be stroked, and the infants would bite at her ankles or pull at her skirt, trying to lure her into joining in their play.

Through months of observing the same langurs, Mrs. Jay came to know how each of the females would behave to the infants and how the infants would respond. The following account is drawn entirely from her intensive study.

As a langur mother holds her baby, cleaning and inspecting its body, the other females gather around. Their curiosity is intense and their desire to hold the infant is so strong that they wait in line for their

How Langurs Communicate

As a langur grows up, its social behavior, including the kinds of
noises and gestures it makes, keeps changing. As a newborn infant,
it can only whine and squeal. At the "infant 2" stage (from five to
15 months), it begins to be able to rage, scream and make faces. As
a juvenile, it gradually stops its babyish tantrums, and starts to
pick up more adult means of communication, such as barking in
alarm and bobbing its body as a threat. True aggressive barking
and fighting for dominance are reserved for subadults and adults.

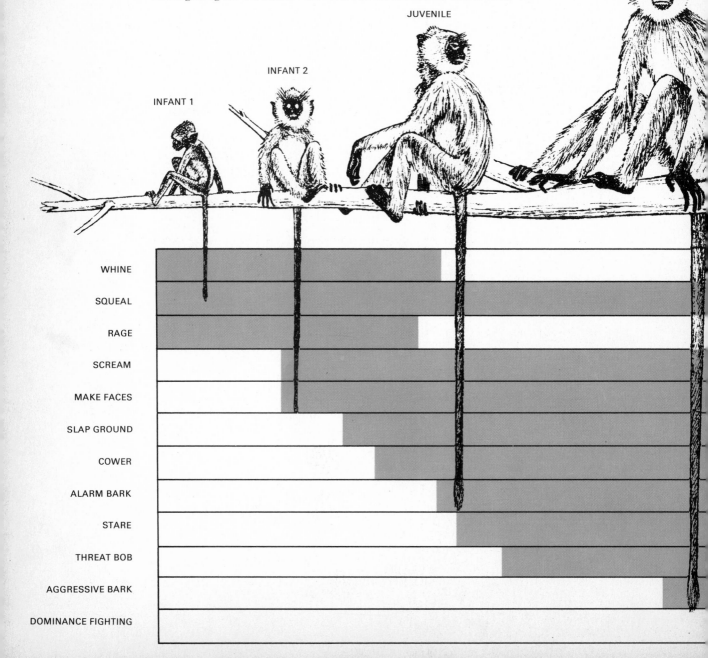

SUBADULT

JUVENILE

INFANT 2

INFANT 1

WHINE

SQUEAL

RAGE

SCREAM

MAKE FACES

SLAP GROUND

COWER

ALARM BARK

STARE

THREAT BOB

AGGRESSIVE BARK

DOMINANCE FIGHTING

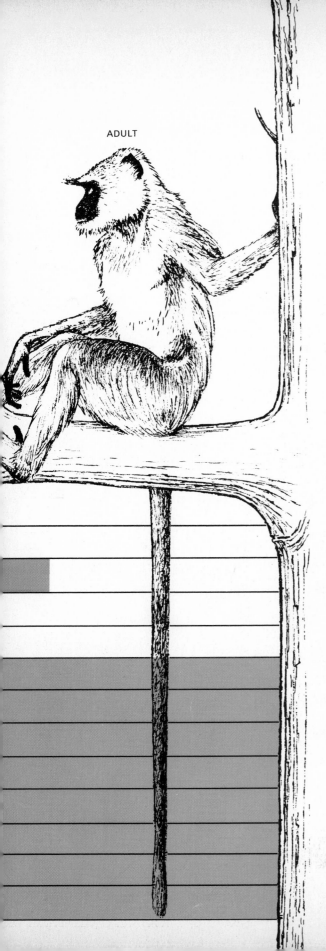

ADULT

turn. A few hours after a baby langur is born, the mother allows other females to take it, but her attention rarely wanders from it for more than a few seconds. She will take it back at the first signs of distress, or whenever she just feels like holding it. Her right to do so is unquestioned. If ever the group is alarmed, she dashes to the infant, scoops it up and races into the nearest tree. She is able to do this easily because the infant is so eager to have her hold it. Soon after its birth, it learns to recognize her and will stretch out its arms toward its mother whenever it sees her approach.

The other females are not merely curious about the new-born infant; they are also extremely protective. Their claim to hold it depends largely on whether they can keep it contented. If it begins to squeal or shows the least sign of discomfort, and if its mother is not nearby, another female will take the infant from whatever monkey is holding it. The female's very strong protective feelings are aroused by, among other things, the infant's movements and cries. But the hair color of the baby also plays its part. For the first three to five months, a langur is distinguished by its dark coat, which contrasts with its pink face, hands, feet and ears. Even if its tiny size did not command the attention of the females, its distinctive coloring would.

Once a growing infant's coat changes color—from dark to light—the attitude of the other females changes. They still come to

71

A Bright-eyed Babyface

A young Ceylonese gray langur has the large ears
and eyes that unmistakably set off infants from
adults. Though its dark face and gray fur show
that it is over five months old, enough of its baby
traits remain to ensure that its mother will still
provide it with food, protection and transportation.

its aid if it is mistreated, perhaps by a playful older infant, but they no longer want to hold it. Its mother, of course, remains tender and protective, and the infant is never far from her.

All the while, the infant is learning. Many people think that all animals know by instinct what to eat, where to wander and which enemies they must avoid. So far as monkeys are concerned, this belief is completely wrong. The infant must learn all that is essential to its survival, such as what it can eat and what it can not. Just as a young child copies its mother's actions, so does an infant monkey. When seeking food it stays close beside her, picking the same plants and leaves that she does.

Observation of others—including the mistakes and misfortunes of others—produces a kind of group knowledge among monkeys that is very useful to them. For instance, one group of baboons living in Nairobi Park, in Africa, had long become used to automobiles. But when two members of the group were shot by men from a car, all the rest of them became extremely suspicious of all cars. Eight months later it was still impossible to get near them by car. In the same way, other groups of baboons have learned to flee into trees when threatened by lions, but to come down out of them and run away when threatened by men—although it may have been years since the group was shot at. From their elders, the younger members have learned what they should avoid, and they seldom forget.

A mother monkey must learn, too, how to be an effective mother. Long before the females become mothers they learn how infants should be treated by observing their elders. Langurs gain practical experience by holding and looking after the infants of other females. This does not mean that all monkeys are naturally good mothers. Experience helps, of course. A mother who has had four infants is likely to be a very good mother. Relaxed yet firm, she holds her baby almost as if she did not notice its frequently violent struggles. But there are some females—nervous, uncertain or irritable—who never make good mothers. They are continually jogging the infant around. The unfortunate infant is likely to grow up to be insecure and irritable itself.

As soon as it can walk with ease, a langur infant starts to venture away from its mother and to play with other infants. While they play, their mothers sit calmly by and watch, like human mothers in a park. If the play gets too rough, they will bring the roughnecks to order with a mild threat. And occasionally some of the mothers will wander away to take a break, leaving one or two behind as babysitters.

It is through play that the infants learn to adjust to their fellows. Since they are social animals, monkeys have to learn the rules. Only by trial and error constantly repeated does a monkey learn how far it can go in threatening or attacking others before drawing punishment upon itself. And the play group is the perfect place to learn because its members are young and their teeth are neither sharp enough nor long enough to inflict serious damage.

Inside this protected environment, the infant learns how to mix. By playing with monkeys its own age, it also develops its personality. The word "personality" may appear somewhat strange when applied to a monkey, but monkeys do appear to have personalities. Like humans, they can be social, antisocial or, when kept in captivity, positively unable to cope with society. If they do not receive enough of the right kind of care in infancy, they will never be able to mix properly with other monkeys.

This too has been established by Professor Harlow in experiments. It is obvious, from watching monkeys in the wild, that they play a great deal. As practically every major activity a monkey indulges in serves some useful function, it follows that play too must be important. But how important? The only way to answer that question is to deprive monkeys of the opportunity to play and see what happens; and that is exactly what Harlow did.

First he raised several groups of monkeys from birth without giving them a chance to play. Some groups were brought up in total isolation. The others were raised, each in its own cage, in sight of other young monkeys but without physical contact with them. The results were utterly disastrous.

All the infants in both groups began to act very strangely and some actually developed a form of mental illness. Some sat blankly in their cages, staring into space. Others clasped their arms and rocked and swayed hour after hour, or sucked at their thumbs or fingers, or pinched repeatedly at their skins. And some when approached by humans chewed and tore at their own bodies in terror until they bled.

After varying lengths of time, Harlow brought them into contact with other monkey infants. Those raised in isolation were simply terrified, completely unable to make any kind of social contact. The infants raised in sight of other monkeys did a little better: they did succeed in establishing some kind of social relationship, but the relationships were thoroughly unsatisfactory. The infants fought savagely and showed almost no sign of friendliness.

These experiments suggest two conclusions. To a monkey in the wild, a mother's care is essential for its survival. But, as far as its social life is concerned, playing is apparently much more important. Being allowed to play with the "other kids" is what produces a well-adjusted monkey.

To think of monkey play entirely in human terms, however, can create a false impression. The play of monkeys is much more vigorous. By the time a langur is a year old, it can run up a tree trunk, race along a branch and leap over to another tree with more ease than a human acrobat.

A Bouncing Mother and Child

Carrying her infant around her waist, a female
sifaka bounds off the ground with a powerful kick.
Mother sifakas like this one often travel through
the trees in flying dives covering 30 or more feet;
the young ones must hang on for their lives.

The play of infant monkeys closely resembles that of 10-year-old children. They wres-
tle and they chase each other. They play
Follow the Leader, climbing up to a height
to jump down perhaps into a pool, as infant macaques do. Young chimpanzees even
play Tug of War, using a twig as the rope.
Infant gorillas have been seen playing King
of the Mountain, with the "king" kicking
those who tried to dethrone it, and stamping
on their fingers, though without inflicting
any real damage.

All this tremendously energetic scamper-
ing around is more than just the natural
exuberance of youth. It prepares monkeys
and apes to cope with sudden emergencies
that one day might mean the difference between life and death. The ability to react
with extra speed and precision in emergencies is essential to survival, and it is
acquired through long hours of play.

Until it is about a year old, a langur's
life must be an extremely pleasant one. It
is protected and carried by its mother, treated with tolerance by the adult females,
and regarded at worst with indifference by
the rest of the group. The process of being
weaned must therefore come as a profound
and unpleasant shock. At first the youngster
reacts as if it simply cannot believe that
its mother—that living, protective mother
—is actually rejecting it. When it runs after
her, she runs away. If it persists, she may
slap it. The infant throws tantrums. It
screams, slaps at her, beats its head on the

(*Text continued on page 78*)

A Sense of Security

The tired infant langur (*left*) and
the hungry little baboon (*right*) are
already old enough to scamper about
and poke their fingers inquisitively
into the world around them. But they
never venture far, and always come
back to their mothers' sides. This
close contact with their mothers
provides food and another of life's
necessities: a sense of security.

ground. Lying beside her high in the trees, it lets an arm and a leg dangle loose. "Look," it seems to be saying, "if you won't let me nurse, I'll kill myself. Yes, I will, too."

For several months the struggle continues, quietly ignored by the rest of the group. Though the infant's cries of distress sound, to human ears, exactly like those which at an earlier stage would have brought an adult racing to its aid, they now fall on deaf ears. Eventually the mother wins, but having to resist her infant's indignant and persistent claims seems often to impose a severe strain on her nerves, making her exceedingly irritable and very bad company for the rest of the group.

The weaning period signals the end of childhood. For a while the young langur, now about 15 months old, continues to follow its mother around and may even still ride on her, clinging to her belly. But several months after the weaning is over, its mother gives birth again and her older offspring must make its own way in the group.

From this stage on, young langurs become segregated by sexes in a way that once again recalls human society. The young females stay near the center of the group, mixing more and more intimately with the adult females and their infants. Holding the infants and sometimes tending them while the mothers are away, they are gaining experience toward their own future role as mothers. The young males, meanwhile, spend most of their free time playing. As they grow older, their play becomes more vigorous, and needing more room, they drift away from both the adults and the infants.

Through their play the males establish the close social bonds that will later help to keep the group unified. As they compete for food or for the best sleeping places or the easiest passageways through the trees, they gradually establish the order of dominance they will carry with them into adult life. Gradually too they begin to have more contact with the older members of the group. By the time their period of adolescence finally ends, both females and males have become equipped to take their places as fully adult members of the group. Without any formal course of instruction, they have learned all they need to know.

Time to Find Your Own Food

Ignoring her infant's pleading paw, a female langur concentrates on eating a mango. Sharing food after the baby is weaned is not one of her maternal duties. The infant must learn to choose its own food by copying her. Even after mastering this new ability, it is still under its mother's watchful eye.

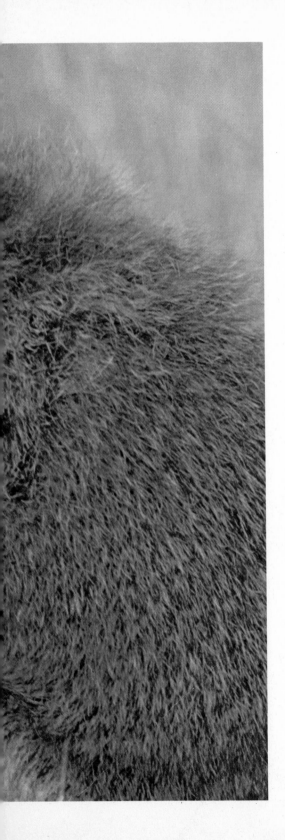

5

Power, Politics and Family Life

On the side of a steep mountain on the Japanese island of Kyushu lives a group of macaques—the monkeys of Takasakiyama. They have split up now, but in 1952 they formed one single integrated unit, about 200 strong. Their discipline was surprising. In the morning the group would set out from its sleeping sites on the upper slopes of the mountain to a feeding station established by Japanese zoologists at the base. They walked always in the same order: the young males frolicking on ahead and at the sides, the dominant males in the center, together with the females and infants. They fed always by rank: the dominant monkeys first, then the others in descending order of status. And at rest the dominant males, surrounded by females and infants, occupied the most attractive area in the middle of their feeding station, where

AN AFFECTIONATE THREESOME—a nursing infant, a grooming female and an adult male— demonstrates the peaceful relationships within a baboon troop. Because of the attraction they hold for adults, infants make even the most aggressive males gentle, and grooming has the same effect.

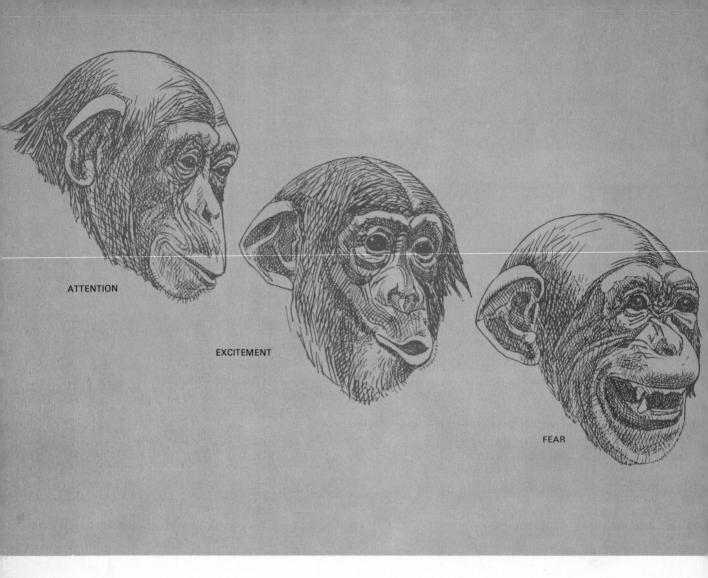

ATTENTION

EXCITEMENT

FEAR

no other males were allowed to set foot.

There is no mistaking a dominant male macaque. They are superbly muscled. Their hair is sleek and well groomed; their walk is calm and majestic. They seem not to notice the lesser monkeys, which scatter at their approach. To block the path of a dominant male is an act of defiance, and macaques learn at a young age that such challenges draw heavy punishment.

To be dominant means to a monkey that it gets the best of everything. It is easy to test the status of two macaques: toss a desirable object between them and see which

one takes it. Once, for example, a tangerine was thrown midway between Jupiter and Titan, the two most dominant males of the Takasakiyama group. While Titan remained still, Jupiter, showing no sign of hurry, walked calmly over and took the tangerine. Another tangerine was thrown, this time right between Titan's feet. Once more Jupiter padded over and took it while Titan stood motionless. Later, another tangerine was thrown and it rolled several feet away from Jupiter to the number-five male, Monku, who was unwise enough to stop it. To Jupiter, Monku's act was sheer defiance.

A Chimpanzee Shows Its Emotions

Chimpanzees, like human beings, make different faces to express different feelings. When paying close attention, a chimp purses its lips in a look of concentration (*far left*), just as a child might. When it is excited, the chimp opens its lips in an O shape. If frightened, the chimp draws its lips back over its teeth and if angry, sticks its upper lip out. The expression for joy is almost human, and the one for sadness is remarkably like that of a crying child, with one exception: chimpanzees cannot shed tears.

ANGER

JOY

SADNESS

Jupiter rushed at Monku, who promptly fled. This kind of symbolic show of power saves the stronger animals from wasting energy, and the weaker ones from suffering unnecessary pain.

One would imagine that in the forests or on the open savanna a baboon, say, could have all the space it wanted. Actually the amount of space a baboon can command directly reflects its status. A dominant baboon occupies the best site when a group is resting, and asserts its right to more space than its inferiors. It can invade an inferior's space as a right, whereas no inferior would dare venture into its space without first making a gesture of appeasement—such as a smacking of the lips—to show its intentions were friendly; it "knocks at the door," so to speak, before entering. If the dominant monkey is in an irritable mood, the others give it a wide berth. If it is feeling amiable, they come closer. One can, after all, sometimes "chat with the boss."

Grooming is perhaps the most common form of social contact between monkeys and apes. One monkey grooms another by picking through its hair to clean out dirt

83

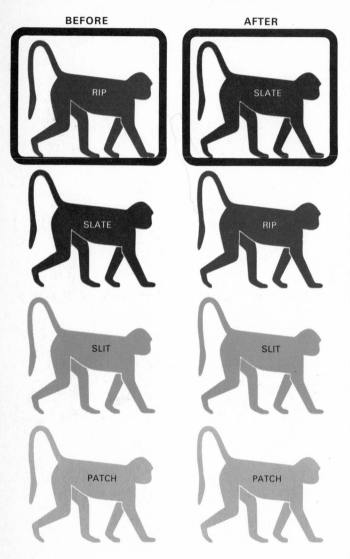

BEFORE   AFTER

RIP   SLATE

SLATE   RIP

SLIT   SLIT

PATCH   PATCH

Dominance Among Langurs

How leadership changes in a troop of langurs is indicated in these diagrams, based on an actual field study. At first a langur called Rip was the group leader. Slate was subordinate to Rip, but superior to Slit and Patch; Slit could boss around only Patch. But after several months of Rip's leadership, Slate became dissatisfied, and pestered Rip with whoops and belches. Finally, after three weeks of this kind of pressure, Slate took Rip's place. Slit and Patch were unaffected by the change.

and parasites—which it does most effectively. To chimpanzees and gorillas, whose social relationships are comparatively relaxed, grooming is largely a form of hygiene. They do not spend much time at it, and they normally groom only that part of the hair another animal cannot reach for itself. In contrast, the more aggressive baboons and macaques have adapted grooming to serve as an instrument of social harmony. Much as humans gather in conversational groups, these monkeys gather in grooming groups. The same function is served—the maintenance of friendly social relations.

The existence of social ranking helps to assure order and discipline, and these things are important among monkeys just as they are among humans. They permit, first, the making of quick decisions. Every jury needs a foreman; every football team, a quarterback. The same is true of monkeys. Some animal has to decide when the group will move, which direction it will follow, what action it will take to avoid enemies. Some form of leadership is vital to avoid indecision or the long arguments that inevitably result if everyone is equal.

A strict social order also helps preserve the peace. Total equality leads to total confusion in any group of primates living in close contact with each other; if the primates are of an aggressive type, this would mean continual turmoil. The strictness of the social order varies therefore with the aggressiveness of the species. Tree-dwelling monkeys, such as langurs, are organized into relatively relaxed orders. A dominant langur will assert itself over its inferiors; it will push them aside to get the best sleeping site or the right of way along a trail. But langurs assert their status more by bluff than by force, and they almost never get involved in actual fights. Gorillas, too, maintain an effective order without violence. Every group has a leader, and each subordinate has its own status. But although the gorillas inside a group may squabble and bicker, as langurs also do, they seldom if ever settle arguments by force.

Baboons and macaques are quite another story. These monkeys have acquired an aggressive temperament as a defense against their enemies, and aggressiveness cannot be turned on and off like a faucet. It is part of the monkeys' personalities, so deeply rooted that it makes them potential aggressors in every situation. A macaque does not struggle to dominate its fellows because it consciously desires to sit at the center of the group and enjoy its pick of the females. It dominates every monkey it can because it is a fighting animal. This urge to dominate means that any group of baboons or macaques is constantly threatened by conflicts within the group. The monkeys live at peace only because that peace is enforced by the dominant males. These males not only defend the group against outside attack, they also act as a police force; whenever a squabble breaks out, one of them is likely to come running over to stop it.

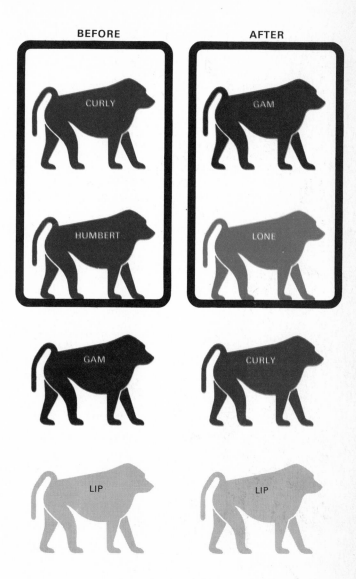

Dominance Among Baboons

Baboons are more aggressive than langurs, and often team up to rule. In this case the group's leaders, Curly and Humbert, helped one another whenever another male, such as Gam, challenged their leadership. But one day Humbert disappeared, leaving Curly without an ally. When Lone, a member of a different baboon group, showed up and allied himself with Gam, Curly could no longer defend his position. He was ousted and Lone and Gam took over. Lip remained at the bottom of the ladder.

85

A dominant male macaque or baboon does not usually have to use force. No society could survive if its rulers had to use all their strength all the time to impose order; there would be nobody left to govern. If the dominant males, for example, used the full power of their big teeth, they would soon kill off the rest of the group. Instead, they preserve order through a system of symbolic threats backed up by their teeth, which play rather the same role as the gun in a policeman's holster.

The elaborate system of dominance and submission, of threat and surrender, is like a parody of relations between humans. When a dominant male is annoyed by a squabble, he glares at the offenders much like a schoolmaster enforcing order in class. His subordinates display submission, looking away like a weak man trying to avoid the challenging glance of a bully, or crouching like a schoolboy begging a stronger boy not to hurt him. The dominant male walks with an air of authority, like a general; its subordinates, carefully stepping out of its path, could be junior officers. Its decisions, like those of a corporation president, go largely unquestioned because no one wants to disagree with the boss.

Since the dominant males get the best of everything, why do the subordinate ones put up with life inside the group? Why don't they leave? Why does the group stay together in the first place? The principal element that holds a group together is the

If Looks Could Kill

Although male baboons continually challenge each other's leadership, the squabbles are usually settled not by fighting, but by fierce displays of teeth. The young male at right is proving its superiority in just such a way. But the old male above, though still putting on a good show, has lost. A younger baboon, whose tail is seen at left, has shown its contempt by turning its back and walking away.

Handling a Fresh Baboon

Occasionally one of the younger males in a baboon troop gets too big for its britches. In the example shown here, one began annoying an older female. In the photograph above, the female *(center)* appears to be appealing for help to an older male, as the younger male circles warily at the right. Apparently the older male agrees to help. Now that she has an ally, the female turns on the youngster *(below)*. Realizing that he is outnumbered, the offender turns tail and runs off at top speed for safer ground.

urge to protect and to be protected, and to enjoy the sense of ease that comes from living among familiar faces. To monkeys, as to people, old friends are the best friends. Most important of all, the group provides a secure environment in which young monkeys can grow up in safety until they have learned enough and are strong enough to take their own places in the group. Gorillas live in little day-to-day danger, so individual males feel free to go off on their own, and many do, even for weeks at a time. The more its members are threatened, the closer the group sticks together. Chimpanzees, which are also in little danger, apparently split into small units whose membership constantly changes. They do not seem much concerned with the general safety; when alarmed, an individual chimpanzee will often run off without giving a warning call.

This would never happen among macaques or baboons. However put-upon it may be, a baboon or a macaque is absolutely loyal to its group and with few exceptions passes its whole life in the group into which it was born. And it does not suffer very much. Group discipline may be firm, but the life of a subordinate baboon or macaque is not so bad. Living together from birth, the members of a group learn how to get along. The ones that cannot stand each other keep at a distance. When tensions do arise, the monkeys involved usually stay apart until tempers have cooled. Only the attempts of one male to displace another in the social ranking will start really vicious fighting, and such occasions are rare; they crop up once every few months inside even a large group. Because every monkey knows its place, daily life is fairly peaceful.

It is uncertainty that creates conflict. The hamadryas baboons in the London zoo fought savagely largely because they were strangers trapped and brought together from different groups, and too closely confined to avoid each other until their differences could be settled peacefully.

Whatever the cause, quarrels are always disruptive, and continual disruption would endanger the group's safety. The peace therefore must be maintained, and among baboons and macaques, peace is simply another word for preservation of the *status quo*. Like the rulers in a human society, it is the dominant males who have the greatest vested interest in preserving their hard won privileges. One of the most intriguing things about baboon and macaque social life is that the dominant males form a ruling clique, acting together for greatest strength. Individually, a member of the clique might be defeated by some male outside it and the *status quo* seriously disturbed. Therefore, the members of the "Establishment" back up each other. When a subordinate male of the Takasakiyama group, thinking that no dominant males were around, was unwise enough to venture into the feeding area and bite a female, he was instantly attacked by the number-three male, Pan, who happened to be sitting behind a rock. Pan, enforcing the power of the elite, was immediately backed up by two other dominant males, and together the three severely injured the rash intruder.

This system of rule-by-clique is peculiar to baboons and macaques, and one can easily see why it came into existence. Because the monkeys are potentially so aggressive, the peace in a large group can only be preserved by a force stronger than any one animal could command. The clique also helps solve the problem of succession, which bothers monkeys and apes as it does human societies. Rule by a single individual is always hazardous; the murder of Caesar, for example, plunged Rome into anarchy. The same kind of anarchy is likely to afflict non-human primates that rely on individual leadership, as gorillas do. When a gorilla leader dies, the group often splits up, its members going off to join other groups. If the leader should suddenly be killed by hunters, the group may not be able to function in the crisis. "I have seen native hunters," wrote the hunter Fred Merfield, "having dispatched the Old Man, surround females and beat them over the head with sticks. They don't even try to get away, and it is most pitiful to see them putting their arms over their heads to ward off the blows, making no attempt at retaliation."

Any such breakdown in leadership among baboons and macaques, which have many more natural enemies, would seriously en-

danger their ability to survive. The group of dominant males acts as insurance against such breakdowns. If one dominant male falls sick or is injured or killed, the others simply carry on, incorporating other males into the ruling elite as they wish—or of necessity, if the challenge of a subordinate on his way up becomes too strong to be resisted. But how does a monkey get into this clique? The answer seems to be: by much the same qualities that make humans fit for membership in ruling groups.

First of all comes strength—simple brute strength. From the moment it joins monkeys its own age in a play group, the young baboon or macaque is continually fighting and jockeying for position. Later it forces its way steadily up the social ladder, knock-

Disciplining a Youngster

Female baboons are in charge of rearing their young, but males sometimes help discipline them. In these photographs a male, bothered by the antics of a youngster, grabs it and bites its neck (*far left*). The bite is not hard enough to break the skin, but the younger baboon gets the message and cowers (*center*) as the male looks on. Finally the male walks away, leaving the young one squealing in the grass.

ing out rivals like a heavyweight boxer on his way to the top. The battles can be vicious, and they are decided by sheer fighting ability. But muscles and teeth are not the only elements; success also depends on a monkey's drive and self-assurance.

Heredity too is important in gaining entry to the ruling group. Every male baboon or macaque has a mother, and each of these mothers has her place in the female social order. The lowliest females are the ones most likely to be tense, nervous, continually threatened and sometimes attacked by their superiors. It is in this atmosphere that their offspring are raised. Almost certainly, the offspring will take on the attitude they see in their mothers. They grow up with a sense of inferiority. They lack the style, the habit and the attitude of the domineering animal; and, as if these drawbacks were not enough, they also lack a means of entrance into the dominant group.

The male offspring of a dominant female, however, is surrounded by confident, dominant males and females, and acquires the same sense of self-assurance and superiority that its elders display. The family support such a young monkey enjoys continues long past childhood; among monkeys tattooed with numbers for study it was discovered that close relatives—brothers and sisters, nephews and nieces—tend to stick together long after they have become adults.

Despite the cohesiveness of baboons and macaques, however, some males do leave their group if their position in it is made intolerable by the leaders. Possibly their strength makes them a threat to the elite; possibly personal dislike is involved. A male that finds itself in this unhappy position will be subjected to constant pressure, set upon, harassed and threatened. The situation will be familiar to anyone who ever felt himself to be an outsider at school. In the end, the unfortunate male may actually be driven out by force. The number-six male of a large baboon group in southern Zambia was literally thrown out by the top five. The same day, it joined another group, defeated that group's lone male and took over its position—very much like a man who is fired by one company and promptly gets a much better job in another.

More often a baboon or macaque leaves its group because the pressures gradually become so unpleasant that it finds leaving more comfortable than staying. Because groups are so cohesive, a male that leaves one group may have to follow another for weeks or even months before it is finally able to join, and some males probably never do manage to break in.

Yet for all their cohesiveness, baboon and macaque groups do split up. It was sheer size that finally split the Takasakiyama group. Quite peacefully, when the group had grown to more than 500, some of the females took their infants and left the central feeding area to join the young males at the edges of the group. Gradually the two sec-

The Respect
Due the Leader

CRINGING IN AWE and huddling for protection, three infant baboons respond immediately as a male leader approaches. Wherever he goes, such a male commands the respect of all members of the troop.

WRESTLING PLAYFULLY, the infants that only a moment ago were cowering are no longer afraid. By sitting down, the male assured them of his friendly intentions; as fierce as they sometimes seem, males often play with the young.

tions drifted farther apart. They left to eat at different times, and spent less and less time together until finally the seceders chose a separate area to sleep in, and the break became complete.

That split was peaceful. The dominant males remained together; the breakaway group was led by six young males, one of whom became the leader. But the breakup of a group can also be set off by arguments among the dominant males. In another group of Japanese macaques, the split was triggered when the number-three male was displaced by a rising young aggressor. Following this shift in power, severe fighting broke out in the group, and a quarter of the animals stopped coming to the feeding place. Led by the deposed and rebellious Number Three and by another, younger male, they formed a separate group of their own. Significantly, the rebellious monkeys obeyed the rules of dominance much more rigidly than the original group had done— as often happens in human society after a revolution, when the rebels emphasize discipline to counter the anarchy that is so likely to accompany rebellion.

A Youngster On Its Own

No longer the center of attention it once was, a two-year-old baboon sits alone, studying a bit of stubble. The youngster is old enough to fend for itself, and it must be able to make its own way in the society of the troop—an important process that will determine its role for the rest of its life.

GATHERING AT DAWN, a troop of baboons prepares
to move into a feeding area. At night baboons sleep
together in trees as a protection against attackers.
Though they move around day by day, their range
is seldom bigger than 15 square miles. Here they
find enough food, water and trees for refuge.

6

The Group and
the World Outside

"Man is born free," wrote the philosopher Jean Jacques Rousseau, "and everywhere he is in chains." They are, if nothing else, the chains of habit. Most of us eat at the same times every day. We sleep the same regular hours, take the same route to and from work, and live in one place for much, if not most, of our lives. How different, we imagine, is the life of the monkeys and the apes! They are free. No time clocks or commuter trains for them. They can eat or sleep whenever and wherever they please, stay in one place as long as they wish, wander throughout the forest at will.

Such a picture could hardly be further from the truth. Compared to the life of the average suburbanite, the lives of monkeys and apes are monotonous, repetitious and humdrum. They pass their entire lives in the same small group of companions. They never venture beyond one tiny area of the forest or the savanna. And they follow daily schedules almost as regular as those followed by many men.

Except for one South American species (the douroucouli, or owl monkey) all monkeys and apes are daylight animals. Their day begins at dawn. Like many humans, they tend to be sluggish when they first awaken, but very soon the youngsters, then the females and last of all the adult males liven up and start to feed. This, the first meal of the day, continues for some time, interrupted only as the group moves, in search of food, along some familiar trail. Toward midday they break off for a rest. The adults nap or groom each other or just laze in the shade, while the youngsters play.

Eating brief snacks throughout the day, the group starts in on its second period of intensive feeding in the late afternoon, continuing to eat steadily for perhaps two hours. Then as evening approaches, the group slowly begins to make its way back along the ground or through the trees to one of the regular sleeping sites, where it will pass the night. One by one, the members of the group climb out to their sleeping places. Gradually their activity dwindles away and, by the time darkness descends, all the animals are asleep.

The attachment of monkeys and apes to one tiny domain is another symptom of their conservatism. The domain, of course, is a three-dimensional one. Different foods and different living conditions exist at all levels in the forests, with each species staying fairly close to the level that suits it best. Gibbons and orangs, howlers and colobus monkeys spend almost their whole lives near the top canopy of the forest. One type, the timid olive colobus, stays 20

feet from the ground. It seldom sets foot on the forest floor, and climbs higher than 20 feet only to sleep or to avoid predators. Horizontally as well as vertically, the more time a monkey spends in the trees, the smaller is its range. The gibbon, the master tree-dweller, passes its whole life within the same one tenth of a square mile. A group of howlers travels over a range of half a square mile. The common Indian langur, which spends much of its time on the ground, roams farther—from one to three square miles. The greatest wanderers of all are the ground-living monkeys and apes—the gorillas, the baboons and the macaques. Baboons usually walk three to five miles during an average day. During the course of a year they will travel over an area of from 10 to 15 square miles, constantly crossing and recrossing their tracks as they make their daily journeys between feeding areas, water holes and sleeping sites.

What governs the limits of a group's range? The answer is the tradition of a long habit. As they grow up, young monkeys and apes observe unconsciously that their group never wanders beyond certain boundaries, set by a stream perhaps, by a ridge of hills or by no particular landmark at all. Beyond these boundaries lies the unknown, threatening in its mystery. Reluctant to venture there, and conditioned by their early confinement, monkeys and apes continue as adults to stay within the range they have learned to know.

COLOBUS

GUENON

Forest Homes at Many Levels

Monkeys may appear to clamber from the tops to
the bottoms of trees, but actually many of them
spend most of their time at a few special levels in
the tropical forest. Each kind lives at the height
that provides its favorite food. This simplified
drawing shows the levels chosen by different species
of guenons and colobus monkeys. Some monkeys
are so used to their own levels that they never shift
to another one, even for the same type of food.

99

Generation after generation, the same tradition is passed down, and this tradition is reinforced by the sense of security that comes from living in familiar surroundings. Like men and women who feel most relaxed in their home towns, a group feels safest and most at ease in the heart of its home range. There it knows the best feeding places, the safest sleeping sites, the most dependable sources of water. As a group moves toward the limits of its range, its members become progressively more tense, and beyond those limits, they never venture. No one has yet been able to drive a group out of its range. Even prosimians will resist any effort to force them over the boundaries, because their fear of the unknown land ahead outweighs their fear of anyone trying to drive them from behind. The same is true of baboons, as the English psychologist K.R.L. Hall discovered when he and a co-worker tried to drive a group of baboons out of its range; when the monkeys reached the boundary, they turned and ran back, right past the two people who were driving them.

This tradition of limited range is no accident. It is an adaptation for survival. Being in competition for the same food, different groups of the same species might well get involved in suicidal fights if they just wandered freely in and out of each other's feeding places. Inherited tradition helps keep them apart, and it is backed up by a system of signals that is especially useful

Masculine Armor and Weapons

The males among primates that live on the ground must defend the troop, and they are usually larger and stronger than the females. They also have special fighting equipment: larger canine teeth than the females', and in the case of the hamadryas baboon (*at left, above*) a thick mane to protect the shoulders. These differences are slighter among tree-dwellers, which depend on speed to escape enemies.

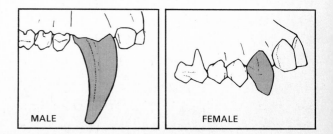

MALE   FEMALE

100

to tree-dwelling monkeys, which, unable to see clearly through dense foliage, might accidentally blunder into each other. As soon as they awake in the morning, the adult males of a howler group set up a steady roar that lasts for up to half an hour. The roar is repeated whenever the group moves from one feeding place to another or when two groups come into contact. Then the males will roar at each other until one group retreats.

Langurs also employ signals—whoops, in their case—to let other groups know where they are. So do gibbons and the spider monkeys of South America, which give warning calls that sound like the bark of a terrier. This kind of vocal signaling is not needed on the ground, where one group can easily see another long before making contact— one reason that ground-living monkeys are so quiet compared to the noisy monkeys that live in the trees.

The care a group takes to warn other groups of its presence is another symptom of conservatism. Only the familiar is safe: strangers are suspect and their mere presence is cause for alarm. Still, not all apes and monkeys are equally worried by strangers. Suspicion is always defensive, a reaction to danger experienced or anticipated, and as we have seen, the species that are most fearful of strangers are also the most aggressive. As one might expect, gorillas and chimpanzees, which have little to fear from predators, are the least perturbed by unfamiliar members of their own species. A chimpanzee group will accept stray individuals. Two gorilla groups will often come together peacefully, and unless the leaders are unusually suspicious individuals, the members of the groups may mingle freely.

Howlers and langurs are more suspicious. Though not in much danger from predators, they do not feel as secure as gorillas. Suspicion of strangers reaches its peak in baboons and macaques—especially in the rhesus macaque, probably the most aggressive of all nonhuman primates. The difference in attitude between the more- and the less-suspicious species was demonstrated very neatly a few years ago when a male and a female macaque joined a group of langurs. The male bore on his face the traces of a healed scar, which suggests that he had been wounded in a fight and either had been driven from his group or had voluntarily decided to leave it. Presumably, being a monkey and therefore highly sociable, he preferred to live among monkeys of a different species rather than be left entirely alone. Why the female accompanied him to join the langurs is a mystery. Whatever their reasons, the two macaques behaved according to form. Though they were hopelessly outnumbered, they established complete dominance over the langurs.

But this was not all. Though they were living among monkeys of a completely alien species, the refugee macaques kept all their suspicion of strangers. At one point, a lone

(*Text continued on page 104*)

Three Patterns for Defense

RESTING AT NOON, a troop of baboons is grouped in much the same order as it maintains while on the march. The more important males, the females and the infants still cluster together, but some youngsters romp on the fringes.

ON THE MOVE, baboons must always be ready to defend themselves against enemies, so they arrange their troop in the pattern shown here. The least important males (*blue*) take the dangerous positions at front and rear. The strongest males (*purple*) watch over the central group of youngsters (*tan and rust*), as well as the females (*brown*) with their babies (*black*) riding on their backs.

CONFRONTING AN ENEMY, the dominant male baboons leave the center of the troop and take up positions out in front, leading the rest of the males into battle against an attacker. Dominant males bear the major burden of defending the troop against animals such as the leopard shown here. Meanwhile, the youngsters and the females, still carrying their babies piggyback, retreat to leave the field clear for their protectors.

male langur appeared on the scene and
started to wander around the edges of the
group, hoping to break in. Acting like a sen-
try, the male macaque would draw the
attention of the male langurs to the presence
of the outsider. Once alerted, the male langurs then joined in repelling the stranger,
and eventually he wandered away.

In the wild, members of even the most aggressive species reach a mutual understanding that takes account of their neighbors'
need to survive. "You keep out of our
hair," is the sense of it, "and we'll keep
out of yours." This live-and-let-live ar-
rangement is essential if physical combat is
to be avoided. For although neighboring
groups normally avoid each other's central
feeding places, they do not necessarily keep
apart altogether. Two or more groups of baboons will often come together to feed out

of the same fruit tree or to drink from the
same water hole. Even when drinking from
the same water hole, the two groups do
not mingle. Normally, the smaller group
will move away when the larger and more
powerful group arrives. But from years of
sharing the same drinking water, the members of different groups may come to know
each other by sight. More likely, the different groups were once a single group, so
that some of the adults knew each other as
youngsters. Two such groups may keep up
a certain amount of friendly play. One
young baboon, for example, often used to
go off and play with young baboons of another group when they met at a water
hole, much as a boy might visit the house
of a neighbor.

The pressures of natural enemies have
led baboons to develop a mutual assistance
program with animals of different species al-

together—principally hoofed animals such as impala and bushbuck, which share with them a common fear of carnivores. Baboons and their hoofed neighbors share an efficient warning system. The baboons have excellent vision and the larger animals have a keen sense of smell. The two groups together are almost impossible to surprise, and a single warning bark will alert all of them to danger. A group of baboons was once seen in Nairobi Park feeding on the side of a hill that was separated by an open space from the dense bushes around a water hole. Two lions came into view. The baboon males gave warning barks, and, within a few seconds, a mass of giraffes, impalas and waterbucks, previously hidden in the bushes, streamed out into the open, where they stood, nervously testing the air, trying to identify the danger.

The baboons' own defensive system is

The Big Males in Action

Crouching tensely (*far left*), the males of a baboon troop mistake a stuffed leopard for the real thing in an experiment. The photograph above shows what happened after a big male lunged at the dummy and knocked it off the log: all of the males, led by the two largest, gathered around to rip their fake enemy to shreds, while the female climbed up onto a branch to scream in triumph. Such teamwork makes a troop of baboons a powerful fighting force.

105

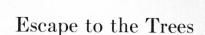

Escape to the Trees

Panicked by hunters, a family of gorillas scrambles into the branches of a flimsy-looking tree (*above*). Full-grown gorillas climb into trees only in an emergency to escape danger. Living almost entirely on the ground, they have lost the nimbleness of other primates. To make up for this, they have acquired vast strength and size—the average full-grown male weighs nearly 500 pounds. Young gorillas clamber about the trees, and often sleep in nests on low branches. But a hefty male like the one at left, carrying a load of leafy bedding, usually sleeps on the solid ground.

an elaborate one. We have seen how, when they are at rest, baboons take up positions reflecting their personal relationships. The dominant males sit at the center of the group, near the females and the infants, while the younger and less dominant males stay out on the edges. When the group is moving, this spacing pattern is maintained. The dominant males, the females and the infants stay in the middle of the marching column, while the other males go on ahead, like an advance guard, or follow behind.

This pattern serves as an instrument of group survival. Going on ahead, the young, powerful males take the brunt of any sudden attack; they are also the least needed members of the group. The defenseless females and infants are closely escorted by the older dominant males, which are best equipped to defend them. If predators do approach, the group will keep moving while all the adult males drop back to form a defensive screen.

A dominant male will also drop back to help a female or an infant in distress. One male was seen to do this for a female burdened with a newborn infant that could not cling properly. Forced to use one arm to hold the infant, this mother lagged behind the group. Whenever she stopped, her male escort also stopped; when she moved, he moved. He never left her unprotected for a moment.

Because defense is essential to survival, baboons learn how to cope with danger with amazing speed, and remember what they have learned. Furthermore, it appears that the frightening experiences of some can be passed along to become part of the experience of the entire group. This ability to pool knowledge is one of the basic advantages of group living, for it means that individual animals do not have to make their own mistakes in order to learn caution. The young especially can profit from the mistakes or the bad luck of others. For this reason a baboon who is killed does not necessarily die in vain. For the way it dies may improve the chances that its companions will survive.

If there is one generalization that holds true of all the monkeys and apes so far studied, it is that they are full of surprises. Consider, for example, the patas monkey, which for years had baffled primatologists. Though adapted to life on the ground, it is neither tough nor equipped to fight off predators, as are baboons and macaques. Instead, it is a slender, long-legged, speedy monkey, which led primatologists to assume that it managed to avoid predators by outrunning them. Then, in mid-1963, the late K.R.L. Hall carried out a study of patas monkeys living in Murchison Falls National Park, in Uganda. One day a group that he was following suddenly disappeared. Although he searched far and wide over the savanna, he failed to find them—until he returned to the place where he had last seen them. And there they were: instead of fleeing, as he thought they had, they had simply crouched down out of sight in the long grass. Nevertheless, under other circumstances—as when a group of baboons is approaching—patas monkeys will use their speed to escape.

Almost all apes and monkeys are afraid of man—even the powerful gorilla. While a male gorilla may pause and beat its chest in brief threat when a man approaches, it will very quickly fade back after the rest of its group into the concealment of the forest. The gorillas' nervousness, of course, makes them extremely hard to follow, and many people had tried and failed to study them before George Schaller succeeded. Undoubtedly his success was largely due to his remarkable patience and caution. Until gorillas were thoroughly used to him, for example, he never looked them directly in the eye. Nor did he point a pair of field glasses or a camera at them in case they might interpret the staring eye of the lens as a threat.

An individual gorilla could still be exceedingly nervous, as Schaller discovered, even when surrounded by other gorillas that had lost their fear. Once, a strange female joined a group that Schaller had been following for several weeks. The other gorillas were no longer at all frightened, but whenever the female saw Schaller, she immediately screamed and dashed away. With some amusement, he noticed that the other gorillas appeared baffled by the violence of her reaction. The female, no doubt, must have been equally mystified by their strange new attitude toward this intruder, a man —the gorillas' one really dangerous enemy.

It is unfortunately true that man is indeed an enemy of other primates. Every year, hunters capture or kill apes and monkeys by the thousands—for zoos, for their meat or skins and for medical research. As man penetrates deeper and deeper into the forests and cuts down trees to open up the land for farming, the nonhuman primates in his way are left homeless. Some species, such as the gentle orangutan of the East Indies and the mountain gorilla of Central Africa, are in real danger of being completely wiped out, except for the few pitiful survivors who may live on in the loneliness and confinement of zoo cages.

A Living Watchtower

The tall giraffe is a valuable ally of the baboons because it can spot predators over shrubs in places where the monkeys cannot see them. Baboons know giraffes are fine lookouts at waterholes—the giraffes take extra precautions before drinking, because their splay-legged stance makes them easy to attack.

7
Studying Monkeys To Understand Man

Man is unique among the primates. He alone lives entirely on the ground, needing no contact with the trees to feed in, to sleep in or to take refuge from his enemies. He alone relies on weapons for defense, uses complex tools and has developed an elaborate culture. He alone systematically contemplates the past and broods over the future, speculates and plans and talks, and thinks in abstractions: good and evil, right and wrong, progress and decline.

Because man does differ so widely from all the other primates, it might seem unlikely that observing monkeys can help us to a greater understanding of ourselves. However, studies of monkeys and apes, conducted in the field, have helped anthropologists to a clearer understanding of some of the most significant aspects of man's history.

Consider, for example, one of the most decisive steps in human evolution: the descent of man's apelike ancestors from the trees. Why did they come down to the ground? What was the reward so great that it lured them out of their treetop refuge? We can understand what may well have happened by studying the monkeys that live in the en-

JUNGLE PLAYMATES, a pet woolly monkey and two young children of the Auca Indian tribe frisk together near their village in Ecuador. To the primitive Aucas, monkeys are a natural and familiar part of everyday life. They are kept not only as pets, but also as a source of meat for the tribe.

Early Views of Primates

Throughout history men have been fascinated by apes and monkeys, and have included them in fable and religion. The ancient Egyptians thought baboons were a sacred link between man (seen praying in the picture at right) and gods (represented by an all-seeing eye). This early drawing of a baboon is quite accurate compared to the illustration at left, from a 17th Century book of natural history. Called a "cynocephalus," or dog-headed man, it was probably an artist's attempt to illustrate tales he had heard of a baboon or lemur in far-off Africa.

vironment that man's ancestors must have occupied several million years ago.

We begin this comparative study with the vervet, one of the most numerous species of monkeys in Africa. Although vervets are still tree-dwellers, they also spend a good deal of time on the ground, and we can describe the process by which they gradually made their descent from the trees. As tree-dwellers, vervets fed, and still do, on fruits and seeds and leaves—all objects that often fall to the ground. At some point, vervets must have begun to go down after them. Then, once on the ground, they proceeded to move farther and farther away

from the bases of the trees, moving out into the open to eat the grasses and insects they found there, until they finally reached their present stage of moving freely between one patch of trees and another.

The fact that they feed not only in trees but also under trees and between trees is certainly a principal factor in the vervets' evolutionary success. Still, they remain at least 50 per cent tree-livers.

To trace the next stage in the evolutionary progress of man's ancestors, it is necessary to move on to the baboons and macaques, which have adapted far more thoroughly to life on the ground.

Why these monkeys should have taken this further step it is impossible to say. Probably the best explanation is that they were equipped with digestive systems that enabled them to eat many different kinds of foods, and found by experience that the greater variety of foods to be found on the forest floor more than balanced the risks of settling there. Baboons and macaques—and also gorillas—survived on the ground because the males developed long canine teeth and other characteristics that enabled them to fight off predators. When man's apelike ancestors came down from the trees, they must have relied on the same type of de-

fensive equipment. Then gradually their behavior changed. Instead of using their teeth for defense, they took to using weapons. This shift, too, is suggested by the behavior of certain nonhuman primates.

Orangs and various other monkeys and apes often throw branches at other animals as an expression of hostility. Man's apelike ancestors, no doubt, also threw branches and rocks at their enemies, and very often the weapons they hurled must have sent those enemies into rapid retreat. Gradually the idea must have penetrated their minds that throwing rocks at a predator could scare it away, and that this was much safer than getting into a tooth-and-claw fight. One favorable experience must have followed another, until finally benefiting from what they had learned, men came to use weapons regularly, first to defend themselves then later to attack animals.

Weapons are simply a form of tool; and tools, as Jane van Lawick discovered, are used by chimpanzees. They will strip leaves from a twig and use them to clean their bodies or to wipe mud off bananas. They also chew leaves briefly to crumple them, then dip them into water when they are thirsty and want to drink. This enables them to draw up seven or eight times as much water as they could by just dipping in the fingers of one hand. Chimpanzees also use tools in a more complex way: they push twigs or grass stalks into termite holes to draw out the insects, which they pick off the stick with their lips.

In another form of activity considered unique to humans, some monkeys and apes behave like man. It is hard to imagine a monkey as an artist, yet some of them can and do paint. Capuchin monkeys, orangs and at least one gorilla have been successfully coaxed into trying their hand with the brush. Chimpanzees, as is so often the case, have proved particularly cooperative.

The results have been intriguing, even startling. Apparently chimpanzees paint very much as a human child does. The English zoologist Desmond Morris observed the work of a young male chimpanzee, Congo,

Skeletons from Monkey to Man

Three skeletons show the development of primates from the four-footed monkey through the arm-swinging gorilla to two-legged man. The monkey's arms are almost as long as its legs; it walks with its hands palms down, nearly flat on the ground. The gorilla, built to move in a crouching stance, is unable to put its palms on the ground, but does use the backs of its hands to maintain its balance. Also, the gorilla can climb with an arm-over-arm motion that is impossible for the monkey. Man's body structure allows him the most flexibility of all. As a baby he can crawl with his palms down; as a youth he can climb through trees like an ape, though much less skillfully. And, of course, man is the only primate who is truly two-legged.

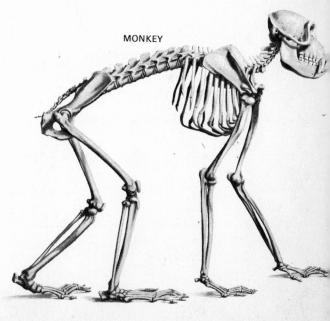

MONKEY

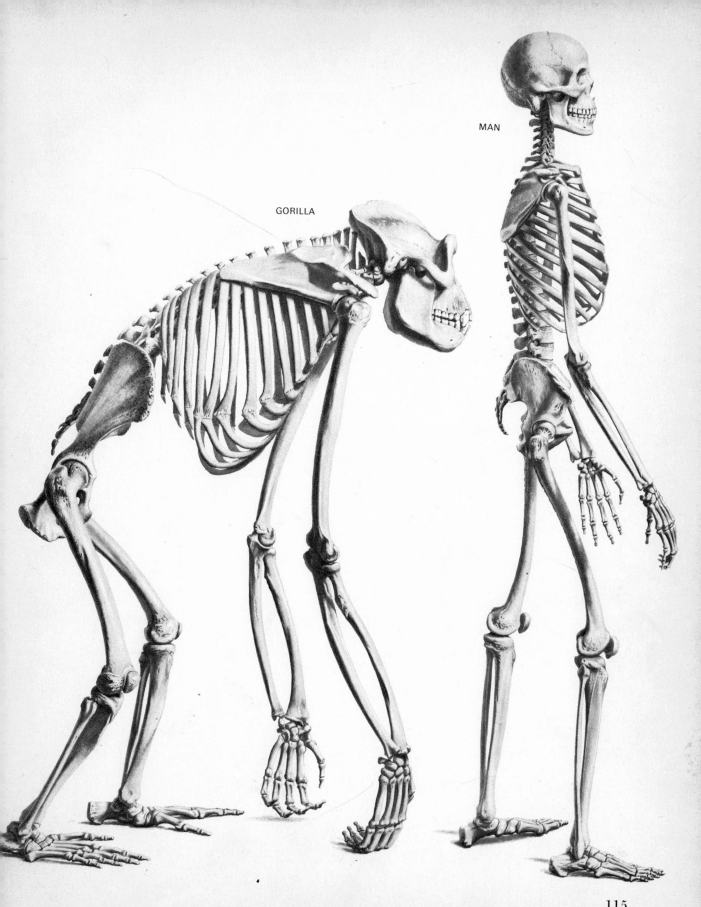

GORILLA

MAN

A Thinking Rhesus

The ability of monkeys to think by relating ideas is shown in this test. A rhesus monkey was first taught to push forward black objects of different shapes every time it was shown a black triangle, and to push forward brown objects when it was shown a brown circle. Then, instead of a black triangle, the monkey was shown an uncolored triangle (*below, left*). Even though the key color was missing, the rhesus still selected the black objects. And when a colorless circle was used (*below, right*), the monkey still picked out the brown objects. The monkey had adjusted—it was able to react to the shape alone.

116

for more than two years. Congo began to paint at the age of one-and-a-half, using at first a primitive, clutching grip, later holding the brush more between his thumb and forefinger. Shortly before he lost interest in painting, Congo was drawing circles and making marks inside them—which is the stage a human child normally will pass through just before he begins to draw faces.

But the really significant point of Morris' study was his demonstration that a chimpanzee does not paint at random. It has a definite sense of form, and even an individual style. Chimpanzees obviously have a talent for painting that can be brought out, and this talent is an early step along the road that finally led to human art.

The study of nonhuman primates can also offer some valuable insights into the operations of human intelligence—for example, into the way human beings learn, and how they learn *how* to learn.

How does a child learn to solve algebraic equations? Or to use language correctly? For several hundred years it was widely believed that while some knowledge is acquired through the process of trial and error, much is accumulated through flashes of insight. Actually, these assumptions were merely theories, for there was no way to put them to the test. We cannot keep a human being in a laboratory in order to trace the development of his learning processes. But as Harry Harlow of the University of Wisconsin has demonstrated, one can do exactly that with monkeys.

Very skillfully, Harlow explored a new method of testing primate psychology. Instead of basing his tests on his monkeys' ability to handle objects—that is, to solve single problems—he based them on the monkeys' ability to discriminate between objects of different shapes and colors. This ability, which must be learned, is absolutely vital to a monkey: it is only through its powers of discrimination that it can pick out food from the surrounding mass of inedible objects. We can assume that the way a monkey learns to discriminate among objects reflects the general pattern of his learning processes.

Harlow began his experiments by putting two objects of different shapes, colors and sizes in front of his monkeys, with a food reward concealed under one of them. After a series of trials and mistakes, the monkeys learned to pick out the object with the food under it every time. Then Harlow used three objects, placing the food under one that was different-looking from the other two. Once again, after a series of trials and errors, the monkeys learned to pick out the object that was unlike the others. Gradually Harlow kept making his problems more difficult, using different colors and backgrounds, until finally his monkeys were performing, practically without a mistake, feats requiring considerable thought.

The monkeys were able to progress because at each new stage they mastered some new principle of selection. Once this princi-

ple was mastered, they were then able to apply it to every similar problem and also to remember it for a year or more. Item by item, the monkeys built up a store of knowledge, just as a child does.

Experimenting in his laboratory with rhesus monkeys, Harlow made some discoveries about motherhood that may bear on human behavior. Why are some mothers loving, others indifferent or even brutal? Monkeys, like humans, are not all born with equal talents. Still, most monkey mothers observed in the wild take good care of their babies, at least during the first weeks of the infants' lives. But Harlow studied four female monkeys that had been raised in isolation without mothers. From them he concluded that a female monkey, if she is to grow up to be a good mother, must herself receive proper maternal care. When the four isolated monkeys in their turn became mothers, they showed none of the attentiveness that a monkey female in the wild lavishes on her offspring. They were reluctant to feed the infants. They seemed not to care when

their young were taken from them, and some treated their infants with positive cruelty. Perhaps human females too must enjoy the attentions of a loving mother if they are to give their own children the love and attention that every child needs.

What happens to the offspring, both male and female, of such unloving mothers? Very much the same as what happens to human children who are raised without affection. The infants of Harlow's "motherless mothers" turned out to be aggressive and to act in other ways like disturbed human children. Even though there are vast gaps between monkeys and humans, monkeys have many of the emotional qualities, both normal and abnormal, of man.

Some 15 to 20 million years ago, several different species of ape inhabited the huge forest that then existed from the west coast of Africa to what are now the islands of the East Indies. Then slowly the climate changed. The forests of the Middle East dried out and became desert, and the great

Fun and Sympathy

A Russian psychologist, Mrs. N. Kohts, tests a chimpanzee to see if it can understand human facial expressions and respond to them. When Mrs. Kohts pouts, the chimp pouts too *(far left);* when she pretends to be sad, the chimp sympathetically chucks her under the chin; when her face shows fear, worry or surprise, the chimp imitates her—or reacts with its own expressions. Finally, the two end their session with a good, hearty laugh *(below).*

population of apes was split into two groups, whose descendants still survive as the chimpanzee and the gorilla of Africa and the orang and gibbon of East Asia. But in between, over an area that covers several million square miles, no apes survive at all. What happened to them? Where did they go? These questions are of vital interest to us because it may well be that their descendants were the ancestors of man.

Between four million and one million years ago at least two varieties of small, apelike men had come into existence in south and east Africa—and, no doubt, across much of southern Asia also. These intermediate creatures, called Australopithecines, stood about five feet tall. Their brains were not quite as big as that of a large male gorilla. But unlike any ape, they could walk in an upright position with their bodies balanced on two feet. Although they had brains much smaller than those of modern man, they were able to make and to use simple tools, probably for hunting.

But even before the Australopithecines, when man's apelike ancestors first descended from the trees, they must have been exposed to attacks from predators and, like male baboons, macaques and gorillas, the male hominids probably had long canine teeth with which to defend themselves, their females and their young. Yet the Australopithecine fossils show that these little apelike men had canine teeth no longer or sharper than those of modern man. They must have lost their long canines because they learned to rely on weapons instead of teeth for defense; this change must have taken a long time to occur.

At the same time, another enormously significant change was taking place. When man's apelike ancestors first came to the ground, they must have relied almost exclusively on their fingers and teeth to obtain food. Then gradually they began to adapt to life on the ground in their own special way. They discovered the value of tools: very primitive ones at first, no doubt—perhaps no more complex than the sticks that chimpanzees use to dig out termites. The important point is, however, that these hominids did not stop there—they went on to develop tools that were much more elaborate and, in the process of doing so, they evolved fingers and thumbs better able to handle the tools.

It was no coincidence that these changes all should have taken place in the same animals, for the shift to two-legged walking and the use of tools were very closely connected. With each new shift toward two-leggedness, the hominids' hands were left more free to make and to use tools. As they came to rely more on tools, they had a greater incentive to depend on their legs for support. So they became even more two-legged. Actually, all evolutionary progress, not only that of man, has taken place through such series of very tiny changes, each one producing some small advantage

Rescuing an Angry Monkey

Pulling a struggling proboscis monkey from the water, researcher Barbara Harrison attempts to bring it back to shore. Conducting studies in Borneo, she patiently rescues lost or homeless monkeys like this one, and takes care of them until they are able to return to their normal lives in the jungle.

and paving the way for the next change.

But chimpanzees use simple tools; why then did they not also go on to use more complex tools?

The answer is that an evolutionary change will occur only if it happens to provide an advantage for the animals' way of life, which depends very largely on where and how it gets its food. Being primarily fruit-eaters, chimpanzees were forced to spend much of their time in the trees, where the fruit is. As a result they kept the kind of hands and feet that were suitable for climbing, and so could not develop the kind of

foot that can best be used for walking on the ground or the kind of hand suitable for complex tool-using.

Perhaps the hominids first began to use tools to dig for food or as weapons to defend themselves against predators. In any case, by the time they reached the Australopithecine stage, they were using sticks and pebbles to kill small animals for food. Instead of being hunted they had become the hunters, and very much more efficient ones than any baboon or chimpanzee.

Hunting was extremely important in the development of man. Together with two-leggedness and the use of tools, it was the

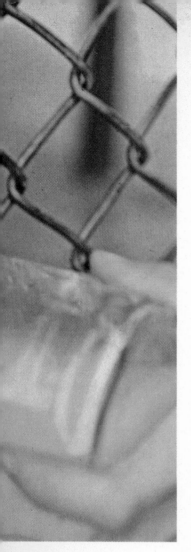

Laboratory Apes

The best way to study primates is in the wild, but laboratory experiments can be useful too. The two apes shown here, at the Yerkes Regional Primate Center in Florida, are helping. The chimpanzee at left happily guzzles its daily ration of orange juice. The orangutan at right, having correctly chosen a red cross over a blue triangle *(top)*, sits patiently awaiting its next test *(bottom)*.

main element that set man on the path to dominance over all other animals. Hunting led the human brain to become larger and more complex. To kill larger animals, man needed to make and to use more elaborate tools, which accounts for his improved control over his fingers and thumbs. He had to prepare his weapons for the hunt, which required foresight. To improve his weapons, he had to recall his past experiences, which required memory. And he also had to weigh what had happened in the past against possible situations that might arise in the future, which called for considerable powers of reflection. What is more, he had to work closely with his fellow hunters. For while an individual Australopithecine could kill a small animal by himself, the hunting of large animals required planning and co-operation. Man had to be able to communicate more complicated information to his fellows, not only for hunting but also for other purposes that grew out of his activities as a hunter.

Hunting radically altered the relationship between the sexes by keeping them apart for long periods. To bring the hunting males together with their females and babies at night, the idea of a meeting place, or base camp, developed. This was a decisive step in man's history. A sick or wounded monkey must keep up with its group as the group searches for food; if it falls behind, it will almost certainly be killed by predators. But now man had only to reach the protection of the base camp and stay there until he got well. A minor disease or injury would no longer be fatal, as it must be all too often to a baboon on the move. It would be merely an inconvenience. Thus men's chances of survival were vastly increased.

By the time man had reached the hunting stage, men and women had a great deal to communicate to each other. Planning base camps, sharing food, reassuring injured companions—all these activities required a system of communication that went far beyond simple expressions of alarm, threat or fear. To meet this need, man retained the system of communication by gestures, facial expressions and sounds used by monkeys and apes; in addition, he evolved a far more elaborate language based on articulate speech enabling him to communicate ideas rather than mere information.

All these advantages had probably begun to exert their influence on human evolution by about half a million years ago. They made possible all the later advances man was to enjoy, notably in the size of his brain and the complexity of his thinking, until finally he became what he is today— master of his planet. As a reasoning, self-conscious animal, man has evolved far beyond any other primate. But reason, after all, is only one part of the fantastically complicated organism that constitutes man. Anatomically, he is not so very different from the great apes. In some aspects of his social life, his behavior resembles that of baboons and macaques. Emotionally, before he grows up and learns to behave as society says he should, he is not so far removed from the chimpanzee.

Certainly man deserves to be placed in a separate family of the primates; he has come a long way since his apelike ancestors left the trees. But not, perhaps, as far as we would like to think, as we look with a mixture of curiosity, awe and a strange sense of uneasiness at the monkeys and the apes that stare back at us—their close relatives—from their perches in the forest.

First Chimp to Conquer Space

Ham, the smallest astronaut, waits patiently with his arms folded as a scientist releases him after his 1961 space flight. Ham wears a chimp-sized pressure suit. Attached to this were devices that measured his breathing, blood pressure and other body functions during his pioneering journey.

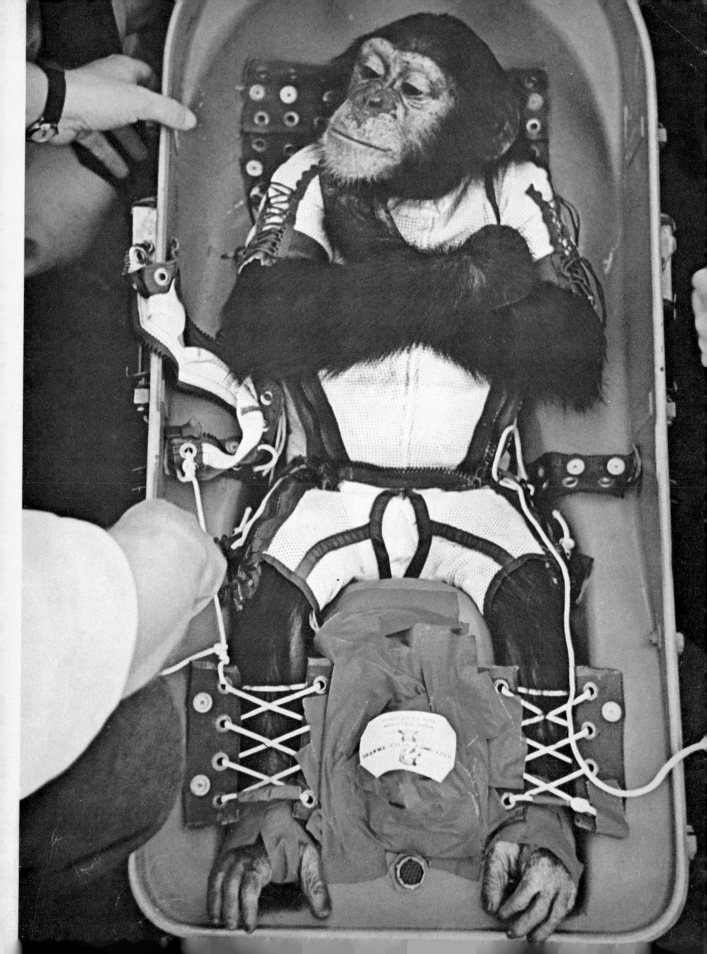

Index

Numerals in italics indicate a photograph or painting of the subject listed.

Credits

The sources for the illustrations that appear in this book are shown below. Credits for the pictures from left to right are separated by commas, from top to bottom by dashes.

Cover—George Holton from Photo Researchers
Contents—Enid Kotschnig—Rudolf Freund and Margaret Estey—Enid Kotschnig—Enid Kotschnig—Rudolf Freund and Margaret Estey—Otto von Eersel—from *Historia Naturalis* by Ulysses Aldrovandus, 1642
6-7—Larry Burrows
8-9—Joseph Cellini
10-11—map by Matt Greene; symbols by Otto von Eersel
12-13—Enid Kotschnig
15—Margaret Estey
16, 17—Larry Burrows
19—drawings by Rudolf Freund and Margaret Estey, photo by Larry Burrows
20-21—Terence Spencer, Loomis Dean
22—Rudolf Freund
23—Loomis Dean
24, 25—W. Suschitzky
27, 28—Nina Leen
30—Mark A. Binn, United Press International
31—Eric Kirkland, Mark A. Binn

32, 33—Larry Burrows, Hedda Morrison
35—Bernhard Grzimek Frankfurt, Rudolf Freund and Margaret Estey
36—E. S. Ross, E. P. Gee
38-39—Walter Ferguson
40, 41—Nina Leen
43—Rudolf Freund and Margaret Estey
44-45—Nina Leen
46-47—Terence Spencer
48-49—Otto von Eersel
50, 51—Ralph Morse, courtesy of Animal Talent Scouts Inc. and L. D'Essen and V. Phifer
52—Michael Rougier
54-55—Enid Kotschnig
56-57—Nina Leen
58, 59—Paul Popper Ltd., Guy Tudor, Terence Spencer
60-61—Enid Kotschnig
63—Courtesy The American Museum of Natural History
64—Nina Leen
66-67—Rudolf Freund
68, 69—Alfred Eisenstaedt
70-71—adapted by Enid Kotschnig from Phyllis Jay "The Common Langur of

North India" in *Primate Behavior: Field Studies of Monkeys and Apes*, edited by Irven De Vore. New York: Holt, Rinehart and Winston, Inc. 1965
72—Alfred Eisenstaedt
75—Loomis Dean
76, 77—Suzanne Ripley University of California Berkeley, Irven De Vore
79—Phyllis Jay University of California Berkeley
80-81—Irven De Vore
82-83—Rudolf Freund and Margaret Estey
84, 85—Otto von Eersel
86-88—Stanley Washburn
90-91—Irven De Vore
93—Irven DeVore—Stanley Washburn
94-95—Stanley Washburn
96—Terence Spencer
99—Otto von Eersel based on drawings in paper by J. R. Napier, Unit of Primatology and Human Evolution, Royal Free Hospital School of Medicine, London
100—Rudolf Freund—Rudolf Freund and Margaret Estey

102-103—Leo and Diane Dillon
104-105—A. Kortlandt
106—*Institut pour la Recherche Scientifique en Afrique Centrale*
109—Sherwood L. Washburn University of California Berkeley
110—Elisabeth Elliot from Magnum Photos
112, 113—from *Historia Naturalis* by Ulysses Aldrovandus, 1642, from *L'Homme et L'Animal* published by Editions Robert Laffont, courtesy the British Museum London
114-115—Jack J. Kunz
116—Enid Kotschnig
118-119—Novosti Press Agency Moscow USSR
121—Larry Burrows
122, 123—Yale Joel courtesy Yerkes Regional Primate Research Center of Emory University
125—Wide World
End papers—Otto von Eersel

For Further Reading

Berrill, Jacquelyn, *Wonders of the Monkey World: Monkeys and Apes in the World.* Dodd, Mead, 1967.
Buettner-Janusch, John, *Origins of Man: Physical Anthropology.* Wiley, 1966.
Clark, W.E. Le Gros, *The Antecedents of Man: An Introduction to the Evolution of the Primates.* Quadrangle, 1960.
Freed, Stanley A. and Ruth S., *Man from the Beginning.* Creative Education Society, 1967.
Lang, Ernst M., *Goma, the Gorilla Baby.* Doubleday, 1963.

Lemmon, Robert S., *All About Monkeys.* Random House, 1958.
McKern, Thomas W., *Readings in Physical Anthropology.* Prentice-Hall, 1966.
Russell, Solveig Paulson, *Which Is Which?* Prentice-Hall, 1966.

Schaller, George B., *The Year of the Gorilla.* University of Chicago Press, 1964.
Scheele, William E., *Prehistoric Man and the Primates.* World, 1957.
Truepeney, Charlotte, *Zephyr.* Scribner's, 1963.
Zim, Herbert S., *Monkeys.* Morrow, 1955.

Acknowledgments

The editors are indebted to John Napier, Primate Research Center, Smithsonian Institution, Washington, D.C., who read and commented on the entire text. The editors are also indebted to the staff of the original LIFE Nature Library volume, *The Primates*, from which this book has been adapted. The staff for this edition was Ogden Tanner, editor; Eric Gluckman, designer; Jonathan Kastner, writer; Eleanor Feltser, Susan Marcus, Paula Norworth, Theo Pascal, researchers; Grace Fitzgerald, copyreader; Gloria Cernosia du Bouchet, art assistant.